Client-centred

BEAUTY THERAPY

FOR NVQ LEVEL 3 AND MAJOR INTERNATIONAL QUALIFICATIONS

IRIS RIGAZZI-TARLING

Hodder & Stoughton

A MEMBER OF THE HODDER HEADLINE GROUP

For my sister Patricia and for Chas, Charles and Anne-Marie.

British Library Cataloguing in Publication Data

Rigazzi-Tarling, Iris
  Business of Beauty Therapy:
  Client-centred Approach
  I. Title
  646.72068

  ISBN 0–340–62104–4

First published 1995
Impression number   10 9 8 7 6 5 4 3 2 1
Year   1999 1998 1997 1996 1995

Typeset by Wearset, Boldon, Tyne and Wear.
Printed in Great Britain for Hodder & Stoughton Educational, a division of Hodder Headline plc, 338 Euston Road, London NW1 3BH by Bath Press Ltd, Avon.

Acknowledgements

I would like to thank all the interviewees for their valuable contribution to the text. Thanks also to Angie Jefferson, dietitian, for her expertise and Mo Rosser for her invaluable help with the exercises in chapters 23 and 24; John Cragg, Director of IPTI, for his assistance with the NVQ detail; and my colleagues and students whose comments have assisted me in writing this book. Finally, my grateful thanks to my dear friend Doris Bunce who typed the manuscript.

The author and publishers would like to thank the following for their permission to reproduce copyright material:

Ellisons: p. 90; Health Education Authority: p. 124; Readers Digest: pp. 196–9; Doctors Magazine: pp. 235–6

and the following contributors for their help with material and for the supply of photographs:

Champneys at Tring, Chesham Road, Wigginton, Tring: pp. 13, 45–54, 147; The Radisson Edwardian: pp. 1, 55, 104, 141, 160, 177; Ragdale Hall Health Hydro, Ragdale, Melton Mowbray: p. 213.

Contents

Part 4 – DIET, GOOD HEALTH AND DIETARY CONTROL

Part 5 – EXERCISE

Part 6 – LIFE SKILLS

INTRODUCTION

The changing world of beauty therapy

Client-centred beauty therapy

The beauty therapy business means hands on, face-to-face, direct communication with your clients. Technical skills form the basis of what must be learned, but communication and life skills must also be acquired.

This book aims to help you to acquire these essential skills, while learning and developing your supervisory skills so that your beauty therapy in practice really is client centred.

The contents closely follow **competences** as specified for NVQ/SVQ Level 3. These areas of competence are also key syllabus criteria for the following major awarding bodies:

- City and Guilds
- BTEC
- SCOTVEC
- International Therapy Examination Council (ITEC)
- Confederation of International Beauty Therapy and Cosmetology (CIBTAC)
- International Aestheticiennes (IA)
- Vocational Awards International (VAI).

The main skill development areas are:

- personal and interpersonal skills
- technical skills (specialist treatments)
- the therapist's skills as communicator and sales promoter
- supervisory and junior management skills, including team leader, appraiser, trainer and businessperson.

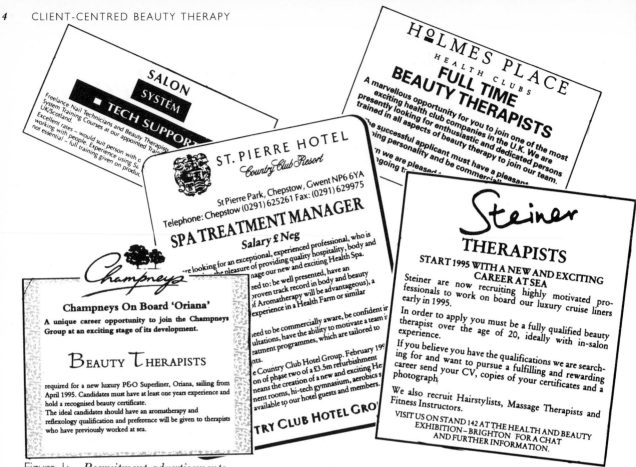

Figure 1:   *Recruitment advertisements*

Client-centred beauty therapy aims to firmly establish the importance of the relationship between **the therapist** and **the client**. In this book fundamental technical knowledge is paralleled with the client's treatment needs, leading to the development of a good rapport.

Industry in Action interviews show the necessity for well-trained therapists who have good all-round life skills. Client-centred beauty therapy is unique in developing the important area of **life skills**.

Industry's increasing demand for multi-skilled therapists means that they must also be knowledgeable communicators who are also client-friendly.

Most countries where beauty therapy is practised demand the high standards as specified in this text. The non-British reader is encouraged to seek all the relevant information suggested in this book, in relation to the country in which she or he is living.

The book is designed to be used as a source of information. Useful addresses appear in the text and are also listed in the Reference Section at the back of the book.

How to use this book

The text has been written under **subject headings** and related to NVQ 3 competence areas.

Students and lecturers can therefore read material related to their chosen syllabus.

Each chapter has Activities spread throughout which are designed not only to test knowledge but to encourage personal skill development and investigation of resources, and to create an archive of useful work-related material.

There is a comprehensive Reference Section at the end of the book which provides vital information related to the subject areas. This gives the student a useful list of addresses and organisations, and a summary of useful information.

The beauty salon

The beauty salon is changing. It no longer is just a place to come to for beauty treatments. It is more and more a centre for health, fitness and diet advice and treatment.

This means that clients expect not just treatments but:

- follow-up advice
- homecare
- exercise plans and advice
- diet information

along with a wide variety of other services to create and maintain the person that they want to be.

The beauty therapist's qualifications

Today the beauty therapist is viewed as a highly skilled professional. The ever-increasing need for better services and skilled operators has placed the beauty therapist in a demanding position. The profession has grown to involve many additional working areas in health, leisure and fitness, so much so that the beauty therapist can now be seen working in a variety of places.

This means that in addition to her/his existing skills she/he will often need to develop a wider range of skills in order to meet the requirements of the chosen workplace. A progressive establishment will offer staff training and be keen for its staff to develop new skills so that the high standard that industry is demanding can be met, but initially a lot of skill development is acquired in the workplace.

NVQs (National Vocational Qualifications) mean that a broader-based training is offered in educational establishments and the workplace.

NVQs demonstrate that the student has received educational training to the level being studied and work related practical experience to demonstrate competence in the skills demanded by that level.

The working therapist must be able to demonstrate competence in a variety of skills including the vital skill of communicating effectively with both colleague and client.

The **Level 3 trained** beauty therapist must be able to work effectively as an

– assistant to more senior staff
– as a team member with colleagues
– as a supervisory person
in the workplace demonstrating multiple skills from

• selling

• training

• management.

The qualified beauty therapist will often want to travel and work overseas.

International standards mean high standards, and well-trained, highly skilled therapists.

Universal qualifications mean a thorough technical, practical and theoretical training, whether you are studying for an NVQ or an International Qualification.

Where does it start?

PERSONAL RESPONSIBILITIES

Whatever position you hold your personal responsibilities will develop according to your role, and as you progress in your career your responsibilities will increase.

EMPLOYMENT REQUIREMENTS

It starts with your **employment requirements**. When you have been accepted for a position you will be working as part of a team. In a large establishment you may be part of a structure like this:

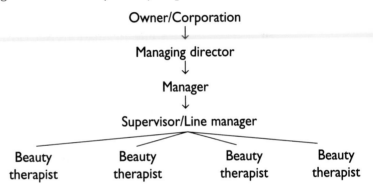

In a small business the structure may be more simple:

Owner/Manager
↓
Senior beauty therapist
↓
Junior beauty therapist

Your position within the business will probably change over time but whatever your role there are some factors that will not change. You have been selected for your professional skills and your presentation. As a professional you are aware that you must practice good hygiene and always be presentable.

This means:

- good personal hygiene
- good oral hygiene
- well dressed in a clean, smart uniform
- short, well manicured nails
- no jewellery (except wedding ring and small earrings)

- hair worn off the face
- low heeled shoes
- light make-up (women).

The establishment where you work will also have professional standards to maintain. These are stipulated by government Acts and must be followed to ensure that the place is safe for staff, clients and the general public.

The relevant government legislation can be found in the detailed Reference Section, on pages 242–261.

The relevant Acts here are:

- The Health and Safety at Work Act 1974
- The Offices, Shops and Railway Premises Act 1963
- The Fire Precautions Act 1971
- Fire Regulations Act 1976
- The Health and Safety (First Aid) Regulations 1981
- Control of Substances Hazardous to Health Regulations (COSHH) 1989
- The Factories Act 1961.

While a company or business should display some important information relating to health and safety and fire evacuation procedures, it is the role of the individual beauty therapist as part of a team to carry out duties that have been directed by the team leader, line manager or supervisor.

The individual beauty therapist will

- follow and practise health and safety regulations as laid down in the code of practice
- use good spoken and written means of communication
- work efficiently and safely to ensure reliable service
- look for ways to improve services and make suggestions/proposals

The team leader/line manager's role is:

- to give direction/guidance
- to carry out duties effectively
- to monitor working systems.

The team leader must ensure that:

- Health and Safety legislation is followed including fire evacuation procedure
- the individual team members are well informed
- all communications, whether spoken or written, are clear, concise and carried out effectively in order to maintain good working relationships
- suggestions/proposals for improvement are noted and passed to the relevant people
- the working systems are monitored regularly.

Working with and supporting colleagues

What does this mean for you?

It means:

- preparing for work
- working under direction
- working together
- working in a supervisory capacity taking responsibility for clients.

PREPARING FOR WORK

Beauty therapists are used to preparing and clearing up after treatments. From the time they start training the importance of good preparation is emphasised. Occasionally in a salon/establishment a more junior therapist may be asked to prepare materials for treatments and to clear away afterwards but generally one can expect to be doing this **at all times**.

The unspoken rule of preparation is **do it**. One should not have to be asked if it has been an accepted part of training.

This means that comments like

> '... who does she think is going to do it ...'
> '... why does he always have to be asked ...'

should never be heard.

You might be assigned various duties that all form part of your job. You might be responsible for:

- wiping the floor after a client if he/she has walked to the beauty room with wet feet
- ensuring clients have turned off taps and showers after use.

WORKING UNDER DIRECTION

When you work under direction it means that:

- you accept that someone else is in charge
- you take instructions and directions and act upon them
- you communicate effectively.

WORKING TOGETHER

Working together side by side with colleagues, as a team, means that you know your role and you are able to work with understanding and practise effective communications so that both colleague and client experience harmonious working relations. Good teamwork means:

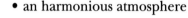

- an harmonious atmosphere
- reliable service
- effective results.

WORKING IN A SUPERVISORY CAPACITY

When you reach this stage in your working role you will have previously experienced working under direction.

You will hopefully have pleasant experiences of this. If not, you will want to ensure that you show all the skill and expertise that accompanies a supervisory position and make sure that those under you have a good experience.

You will want to:

- communicate effectively
- demonstrate good listening skills
- be sincere
- stay calm
- be objective
- take responsibility
- be able to give clear and concise instructions, both verbal and written.

In your position you will be expected to:

- carry out the business' policies and procedures
- organise and maintain written or computer based records and reports

- support staff so that services may be carried out safely and effectively.

Communicating effectively

Whatever your position, if the business is to be successful, you will need to:

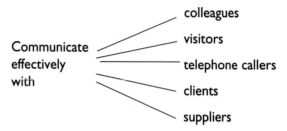

Communicate effectively with
- colleagues
- visitors
- telephone callers
- clients
- suppliers

But how will the following people communicate:

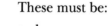

- the trainee
- the assistant
- receptionist
- beauty therapist
- line manager or team leader?

They must all develop certain skills if communication is to be effective.

THE ABILITY TO GIVE COMPREHENSIVE VERBAL INSTRUCTIONS

These must be:
- clear
- concise
- easily understood – given slowly and in everyday language
- spoken in a pleasant manner.

THE ABILITY TO WRITE EASILY UNDERSTOOD INSTRUCTIONS

These must be:
- concise – explain what is being described or required
- readable
- well presented, either handwritten or word-processed.

THE ABILITY TO LISTEN

This means:

- knowing when to stop talking and **listen** to what is being communicated
- listening with interest and understanding.

REMEMBER

You will never appear pleasant and receptive when your **body language** is conveying a different message – eye movements and body stance can give visual communication that will give the opposite message; for further details see page 65.

Design a small card to remind staff about the main points of effective written communication.	Design a small notice to remind staff of the main points for effective verbal communication.

Taking responsibility for clients

The beauty therapist usually assumes immediate responsibility for her client and particularly in the case of an emergency, such as a fire, when the therapist must ensure that the client is taken to a safe area.

The supervisory person will usually take overall responsibility for clients but the individual therapist is encouraged to exercise a responsible attitude towards the client at all times. Clients are in a vulnerable situation in the salon and very much at the therapist's mercy:

- their personal belongings and clothes are locked away
- they are usually only half dressed (in a gown)
- they are reliant on the therapist's expertise.

Responsibility is everyone's business, particularly in a one-to-one working situation.

PART I *In the workplace*

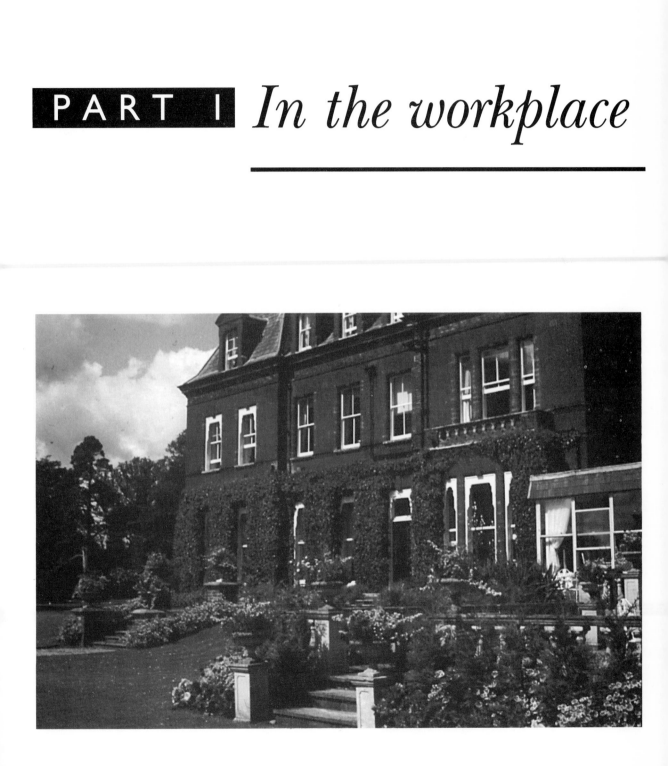

CHAPTER 1 # *Maintaining services and operations*

Supervising staff's daily tasks

When you are working in a supervisory capacity you will have specific duties to ensure the daily smooth running of the business.

These may include:

- ensuring Health and Safety legislation is adhered to
- checking the security systems of the establishment
- checking salon equipment
- ordering of materials and stock
- ensuring that the working environment is **conducive** to work activity
- checking and maintaining work schedules and rotas
- staff support – meetings.

Health and safety in the salon

PERSONAL SAFETY

In addition to salon safety the therapist must be aware of personal safety measures.

The importance of hygiene and protective clothing has already been explained and now the importance of safety whilst working must be considered.
The therapist at work must consider her/his back and look at:

- correct lifting

- correct carrying technique
- correct working stance – in order to balance weight evenly when working, the therapist must consider two stances:
  1 When working the length of the couch the therapist should have one foot in front of the other so that the front knee can bend, and stretching of the body will not occur because a side step can be taken as movement is required.
  2 When working at the side of the client, across the body, the therapist stands facing the side of the body, with legs slightly apart balancing the weight, and thighs pushed slightly forward towards the couch to relieve strain on the hips and lower back.

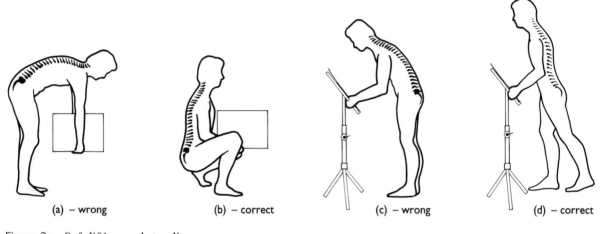

| (a) – wrong | (b) – correct | (c) – wrong | (d) – correct |

Figure 2:   *Safe lifting and standing*

COSHH AND THE BEAUTY SALON

The supervisory person must ensure that staff understand safety, particularly in relation to products and hazardous substances.

Manufacturers often give helpful guidelines.

The following information taken from Ellison's *COSHH and the Beauty Salon* offers the working therapist a basic understanding of the Act and selected information on products and substances.

AEROSOLS

Health hazard: flammable.

Use/handling: Use only in a well-ventilated area. Do not smoke whilst in use. Keep away from eyes. Avoid excessive inhalation of spray. Do not spray onto naked flame or hot surfaces. Do not warm cans or tamper with the valve/actuator to ease removal of contents.

Storage: Keep in a cool dry place. Protect from sunlight. Avoid window displays which are exposed to sun. Do not expose to excessive temperatures.

Disposal: Do not pierce or burn aerosol container. Contents are under pressure and they can cause an explosion in a fire.

Action: In case of fire, evacuate areas known to contain aerosols and inform fire service of their existence.

Beauty products which can be packed in aerosol form are:
Nail dry sprays
Hairspray

AROMATHERAPY OILS

Health hazard: essential oils are extracted from a wide variety of plants and their physiological properties are well known. A professional aromatherapist can be exposed to these oils over long periods. Repeated contact with concentrated oils may cause skin sensitisation.

Use/handling: Always use in a well ventilated area. Book treatments sensibly so that breaks can be taken between treatments. Keep concentrated oils off the skin.

Storage: Store in a cool dry place and out of direct sunlight. Always keep firmly closed.

Disposal: Spills to be quickly mopped up with a tissue or cloth (wear gloves). Ventilate area. Normal disposal methods are satisfactory for small quantities.

Action: Wash immediately from the affected area. Seek medical advice if irritation symptoms persist.

Eye contact:	Rinse immediately with plenty of cold water and seek medical advice.
Skin contact:	Wash area and seek medical advice if irritation persists.
Ingestion:	Depending on the oil and the quantity seek immediate medical advice. Some oils are very toxic if ingested.

FINE POWDERS

Health hazard: inhalation of fine particles can cause irritation.

Use/handling: Care should be taken when mixing powders, filing false nails, applying loose powder make-up etc. Avoid making unnecessary dust. Avoid inhaling even in small quantities. If dispensing large quantities of fine powders a face mask is advisable.

Storage: Store in a cool dry place in a closed container.

Disposal: Treat as domestic waste unless there is a particular hazard e.g. flowers of sulphur is a fire hazard.

Action:

Eye contact:	Rinse with plenty of water. If discomfort persists seek medical advice.
Skin contact:	Wash to remove particles. Seek medical advice if any irritation persists.
Inhalation:	Move to fresh air. If coughing and irritation persist seek medical advice.
Ingestion:	Seek medical advice immediately.

Beauty products coming under this category are:

Acrylic nail powder	Bleaches
Bronzing powder	Calamine powder
Deodorant powder	Face powder
Kaolin	Fullers earth
Nail kits	Magnesium carbonate
Purified talc	Pedicure talc

FLAMMABLE

Health hazard: vapours will catch fire if exposed to flame or other means of ignition.

Use/handling: Do not smoke when dispensing. When transferred into dispensers ensure they are clearly labelled. Use only in a well ventilated room. Avoid excessive inhalation.

Storage: Store in a cool place. Keep sealed. Do not store large quantities together. Some products are less flammable than others – those with a lower flash point are a higher fire risk. See product labelling for further information, i.e. nail enamel remover is highly flammable, solutions containing ethanol such as witch hazel are less flammable.

Disposal: Seek advice from your Environmental Health Officer. Do not flush down toilet or pour into drains.

Caution: In case of fire, evacuate areas known to contain flammables and inform fire service of their existence.

Action:

Eye contact:	Rinse immediately with plenty of water and seek medical advice.
Skin contact:	Wash product off with plenty of water. Seek medical advice if symptoms persist.

Inhalation: Remove to fresh air immediately. If feelings of nausea do not disappear quickly, seek medical advice.

Ingestion: Seek medical attention immediately.

Beauty products which come under this category are:

Acetone	Astringent
Eau de cologne	Equipment cleaner
Flowers of sulphur	Nail Polish thinners
Polish remover	Rose water
Solvents (for false lashes)	Sterex steritane
Surgical spirit	Witch hazel

HYDROGEN PEROXIDE SOLUTIONS

Health hazard: irritant to skin and eyes.

Use/handling: Always wear protective gloves. Avoid contact with eyes and face. Do not use on abraded or sensitive skin. Always use non-metallic utensils, to avoid rapid decomposition of the product.

Storage: Store in a cool dry place away from sunlight and other sources of heat. Always store hydrogen peroxide in the container supplied. It is particularly important that no contamination enter the container as this could lead to decomposition resulting in the liberation of heat and oxygen. Therefore replace cap immediately after use.

Disposal: Dispose of unwanted or contaminated materials down the drain with plenty of water. Do not allow contact with easily combustible materials such as paper. Do not incinerate.

Action:

Eye contact: Rinse eyes immediately with plenty of water and seek medical advice.

Skin contact: Wash skin immediately and if irritation persists, seek medical advice.

Ingestion: Seek medical advice immediately.

Beauty products that come under this category are:
Peroxide
Oxidant

SENSITISING

Health hazard: may cause acute allergic reaction, sometimes quickly, but sometimes only after several exposures.

Use/handling: Keep all known sensitising products off the skin. Use gloves if necessary although the therapist should be able to work without coming into direct contact with the product. Some individuals are much more susceptible to this problem than others.

Storage: Store in a cool dry place.

Disposal: When these products are only in the salon in very small quantities use normal disposal methods. Otherwise contact your Environmental Health Officer for advice.

Action:

Eye contact:	Flush eye with water. Seek medical advice immediately. Take the product and packaging with you to the doctor.
Skin contact:	Remove the product from the skin, wash area thoroughly and seek medical advice if irritation persists.
Inhalation:	Move to fresh air and seek medical advice if nausea and other symptoms do not subside in a few minutes.
Ingestion:	Seek medical advice immediately, taking product and packing with you.

Beauty products that come under this category are:

Equipment cleaner	Nail Off remover
Remover/cleaner	Glue Off
Cidex	Wrap Off
Acrylic nail powder	Tip Off
Curing agent	Pre nail prep
Brush cleaner	Nail primer
Resin gel	Debonder (solvent)
Curing agent	Nail primer
Nail glue	Lashtint

SKIN BLEACHES

Health hazard: may cause skin irritation.

Use/handling guidelines: Use in a well ventilated area and always wear protective gloves. Avoid inhalation of the dry powder and contact with eyes and face. Do not use on abraded or sensitive skin.

Storage: Store in a cool, dry place away from direct sunlight and other sources of heat. Reseal container after use.

Disposal: Do not incinerate. Use water to dilute and mop up spillages. Do not dispose of dry powder, wash it down the drain with plenty of water.

Action:

Eye contact:	Rinse eyes immediately with plenty of water and seek medical advice.
Skin contact:	Wash contaminated skin and if irritation persists seek medical advice.
Inhalation:	If dry powder is inhaled, remove to fresh air. If coughing, choking or breathlessness continues for longer than 10–15 minutes seek medical advice.
Ingestion:	Seek medical advice immediately.

Beauty products which come under this category are:

All bleaches

List five duties of a Health and Safety Inspector or an Environmental Health Officer in relation to the workplace

The Health and Safety at Work Act 1974 requires an employer to be responsible for the workplace and his employees.

List the employer's duties:
a) for the workplace
b) to the employer.

Security

Security means

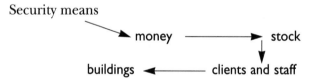

You will have instructions to follow and to pass on to your staff. How will you do this? Draw up a set **checklist** that is used daily? This might include checking that all doors and windows are closed and locked at the end of each day.

If the salon or business has a burglar alarm this will probably be controlled by yourself or another senior person. Staff who are key holders are responsible for opening and closing the business and setting the burglar alarm.

MONEY SECURITY

Most businesses will have some form of **till**. The electronic till offers good security as well as providing a source of valuable information.

An electronic till or cash register can:

• show the correct change

- separate information
- show up errors
- total the day's takings.

When you or another supervisory person 'cash up', that is, add up the days takings, the till will act as a check.

CASHING UP

You will need to record all the sales of the day with the monies taken and leave a **float** for the next day.

A float is a set amount of money which is used to start the till each day.

Staff need training in operating a specific till. This will be your job. Staff may also need to be aware of the necessity for banking takings or transferring money from the till to a safe. Usually only you, or the supervisory person, will handle the safe or arrange the banking.

Handling the safe may be restricted to your manager. Banking you will usually do. Sometimes banking is done daily, and sometimes takings are kept in the safe until the next day.

BANKING

How will you do this?

cheques

credit card vouchers

debit cards

notes

cash

You will need to keep a record of these transactions. Some businesses have large paying-in slips for this purpose.

DATE _____	_____ 19 _____	PAID IN BY _____	bank giro credit

Figure 3:   *A basic paying-in slip*

As the supervisory person it is important to remember that junior staff should receive some training in these skills but always under supervision. In a large company these training skills may be dealt with by a separate training division.

CLIENT/STAFF SECURITY

You will be responsible for supervising your staff and ensuring that they act responsibly both with their own belongings and their clients' personal property.

Clients' valuable property such as handbags, jewellery should be:

* kept with the client, or
* **locked** in a cupboard.

Staff property should be:

* in a locker
* in a 'safe' place – a locked cupboard with a limited number of key holders.

Design a checklist for your staff to ensure that salon security checks are made at the beginning and end of the working day.

CHECKING SALON EQUIPMENT

As a supervisor, this will primarily be your responsibility, although it is the duty of each member of staff to check the machines that she/he is using.

You will need to design a checklist for your staff that records that the machines have been checked. These can be photocopies with all the necessary information, which require regular completion.

A typical sheet might look like this:

Date	Appliance	Serial No.	Working	Fault	Removed	Repaired	Initials

Figure 4:   *Equipment checking sheet*

There should also be a set procedure for dealing with faulty equipment. Who is responsible for getting it repaired? No doubt in your position this will be your responsibility and should be done as soon as possible.

STOCK

It is important that the business does not hold excessive quantities of stock as money (capital) is **tied up** in this way.

STOCK/MATERIALS

This includes:

- equipment, machines, accessories
- towels, gowns, blankets
- consumable products – cotton wool, tissues
- retail products.

You will ensure that staff can:

- receive goods – check delivery notes
- put stock away – know how to store new stock with old stock so that old stock is used first and record new stock levels
- stock check – check the levels of stock.

You will prepare stock record sheets for your staff to complete. You will then put this information into a stock record book or transfer it to a computer. Computer packages offer systems that can:

- record stock
- analyse stock
- calculate your requirements
- forecast and plan your needs.

Both small businesses and large establishments use this computerised method because it:

- saves time
- is accurate
- saves money.

ORDERING MATERIALS OR STOCK

Your job will be:

- to oversee the handling of stock
- to carry out a stock check
- to order stock.

STOCK SECURITY

Retail stock is usually on display to show clients what the salon sells. It can also be a temptation for some clients.

All staff need to be watchful and ensure that it is not easy for clients to remove stock.

You can make sure that:

- display material is not easily accessible (it is stored in a secure display cabinet)
- stock is regularly checked so that anything missing is noticeable.

SALON AND RETAIL STOCK

This will usually be stored in a store cupboard. You and your manager will probably hold the key for this.

Security is maintained by:

- always going to the cupboard yourself, if possible
- ensuring that anyone taking stock from the cupboard completes a stock sheet and that the cupboard is locked immediately afterward, and the key is returned to you.

Draw up a check list to show a junior member of staff what equipment checks need to be made every day.

Design a product stock sheet for your salon, including a column for new stock and a new total stock.

A conducive working environment

Your salon or business will probably already be equipped with the important equipment for an effective working salon.

You will now need to attend to the daily environment. The working environment must be physically and emotionally satisfactory.

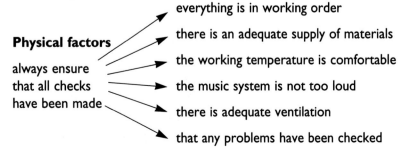

Physical factors

always ensure that all checks have been made

- everything is in working order
- there is an adequate supply of materials
- the working temperature is comfortable
- the music system is not too loud
- there is adequate ventilation
- that any problems have been checked

There are **emotional factors** which will definitely affect the smooth running of the business. These will need careful daily attention and demand all your supervisory skills.

Staff work well:

- if they are happy
- if they receive praise
- if they are not taken for granted
- if they are taught to understand their colleagues' working position.

This means you will need to be perceptive and assess any problems immediately.

REMEMBER

- problems can arise with you
- problems can arise with colleagues
- problems can arise with management policies.

Whatever the reason you must be able to be objective, and stand back and assess the situation fairly.

REMEMBER

A harmonious atmosphere means productive work: that is

- contented employees
- satisfied clients.

CHECKING AND MAINTAINING WORK SCHEDULES AND ROTAS

You will be responsible for creating a staff work rota to ensure that the business is properly operative at all times.

In order for your rota to be effective you will need to consider various points:

- the hours the salon is open
- evening shifts
- Saturdays
- the number of staff
- maximum staff coverage on busy days.

You may have a **fixed** weekly rota or a more flexible two- or three-weekly rota.

In order for staff to be satisfied you will need to consider:

- how many late shifts

• how many Saturdays

they will work.

Once the rota is established it should be **monitored** to check its suitability. It should be flexible enough to allow staff to swap shifts if necessary.

A flexible rota enables staff to plan ahead and have a different day off each week if they wish.

PLANNING WORK SCHEDULES

Staff will need to have a list of duties or a work schedule so that they know what their responsibilities are in the business.

They will need a schedule that shows:

• daily tasks
• areas of responsibility.

These should be clearly stated and displayed in the business so that staff can refer to them.

Careful monitoring is required to ensure that:

• all tasks are covered
• new ones may be added when necessary
• staff are completing the tasks
• the selected tasks ensure the smooth running of the business.

Plan a fixed rota for four beauty therapists in a salon that opens 10.00 a.m.–6.00 p.m. Monday, Tuesday, Wednesday and Saturday, 10.00 a.m.–9.00 p.m. Thursday and Friday.

Plan a flexible rota for the salon described.

Plan a work schedule for three beauty therapists showing their daily tasks and responsibilities.

CHAPTER 2

Dealing with staff

Staff support – meetings

Supervisory staff should hold regular meetings in order to pass important information to the staff. Staff in turn can put forward comments, new ideas or problems arising from their working environment.

Meetings are sometimes held on a daily basis in a large establishment and once a week in a smaller business. As a supervisor you will always need to demonstrate **good leadership skills** and in particular to be **objective**, to stand back to analyse situations and work out your actions.

The person in a supervisory role then reports back to the management so that ideas, proposals, changes in procedure or business policy brought up in meetings can be considered.

Individual staff who need support can be identified and the necessary assistance can be given.

Part of your work as a supervisor is to organise staff training sessions. You are going to organise a session on 'Handling client complaints'.

Explain how you would plan and carry out this task.

You are organising a training session on 'Using and developing existing resources in your salon'.
a) How could you encourage your staff to participate in this training?
b) How would you structure the session so you consider all the necessary information?

Disciplinary procedures

In a **supervisory position** you will probably be the first person to observe a good or a poor working situation or behaviour.

Sometimes the fault may be with the staff. Misconduct and an inability to do the work required are the main reasons for dismissal. But in most circumstances (except **gross misconduct**) the member of staff will be given the opportunity to improve and be monitored before action is taken towards dismissal. When disciplinary action is necessary a formal procedure must be followed in order to conform with legislation.

You will need to:

- investigate thoroughly any suspicion of misconduct or poor performance, depending on the severity of the problem.

You may then:

- initially inform the member of staff verbally; it is always advisable to record the verbal warning in writing.

In your position it may not be strictly necessary to consult your manager or the management before taking primary action. However, it is **always** advisable to do so and to ensure that management is informed in writing.

Your manager will probably permit you to give verbal warnings in the early stages. If the situation does not improve then management will usually take control.

The member of staff in question will then be given the opportunity to respond. Following this, a **staff disciplinary meeting** is then necessary to discuss ways of resolving the problem.

This would probably consist of

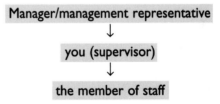

A period of time would be allocated for the member of staff to improve their performance. If there was no improvement a second written warning may be given.

As supervisor, you would be expected to

- monitor progress in written reports
- keep management informed of any changes.

If there was no improvement your reports would reflect this and management would make the decision whether or not to give a **Notice of dismissal**. This would be **fair dismissal** because the correct, legal procedure had been followed.

If, on the other hand you had chosen to tell a member of staff that they were **dismissed** without checking and following the correct procedure, that would be **unfair dismissal** and the member of staff can complain to an industrial tribunal.

Refer to pages 242–261 in the Reference Section for full details of Employment Legislation and ACAS – Advisory Conciliation and Arbitration Service.

Your junior therapist appears to have a conflict with you, the supervisor. Explain how you will deal with this situation.

Write a report on a member of staff who is repeatedly late for her early shift. She has received two verbal warnings.

Staff complaints

You will have to deal with **staff complaints** as well as client complaints.

Staff have to work together and need to do so in a pleasant atmosphere, so it is important to rectify problems as soon as possible.

You should:

- see the individuals and attend to the matter
- record details of your interview for reference.

If a member of staff has a complaint against you personally it is important that they are encouraged to state the problem to you. If this is not possible, ask your superior to deal with the problem to ensure that the matter can be resolved.

A dated, written report should be kept of any complaint, for future reference.

Assessment (appraisal)

The supervisor will be expected to appraise staff. This means that she/he **will monitor an employee's performance**.

As a supervisor you will need to **evaluate your own skills** to ensure that you carry out this task effectively. You will also be appraised by your manager, so you will know both sides of the appraisal.

THE PURPOSE OF THE APPRAISAL IS TWOFOLD

1 To assess the individual's performance by assessing:
- technical skills
- strengths
- weaknesses
- future aims
- potential
- areas for improvement
- further training needs

and encouraging:
- self-assessment
- job satisfaction

2 To allow the supervisory person to:
- give and gain information
- improve communication skills
- give praise and constructive advice
- show personal interest
- target future goals
- identify individual needs
- identify areas for attention
- maintain a productive working environment
- achieve staff satisfaction

You will need to **conduct the appraisal in private**. That means:

- a quiet place
- with sufficient time for the interview.

Your approach and attitude is very important.

You will need to **demonstrate good supervisory skills**. You want your appraisee to:

- relax
- talk freely
- be honest.

You must adopt a similar manner and ensure that you are:

- friendly
- open
- objective
- positive.

Some appraisals may need particular skills and all demand **excellent communication skills**.

You may have an appraisee who has a variety of weaknesses:

- lateness
- poor work record
- poor attitude.

You will need to:

- present the facts
- ask for reasons
- listen.

APPRAISAL/PERFORMANCE ASSESSMENT

What will you need to assess?

How will you want to record it for present and future information?

Performance Assessment will vary depending on the needs of your establishment.

There are many key areas to consider.

These listed below are some of them. You will need to create an appropriate form for appraisal records.

RECORD OF PERSONAL DETAIL

Name _____

Job position/Title _____

Date employment commenced _____

Record of promotion _____

Date started in present position _____

Date of last appraisal _____

Date of appraisal _____

Date of next appraisal _____

ASSESSMENT RATING/SCALE

1	or	A
2	or	B
3	or	C
4	or	D
5	or	E
6	or	F

STANDARDS OF ASSESSMENT

- poor – not meeting requirements of job
- below average – needs to improve
- average/satisfactory
- good
- very good
- excellent/outstanding

ASSESSMENT CRITERIA

JOB PERFORMANCE

Technical skills

Services

Sales

Accuracy

COMMUNICATION SKILLS

Staff

Clients

Colleagues/relationships

Manner – verbal/actions

PERSONAL STANDARDS/APPLICATION
  Timekeeping
  Appearance
  Time off (sickness)
  Initiative
  Confidence
  Job satisfaction

POINTS FOR DISCUSSION
Appraisee
  Career aims
  Career plan
  Training
  Support training
  Improvement
  Plan of action
  Targets

APPRAISER COMMENTS
  Performance criteria/objectives to be achieved
  Development plan/targets
  Training
  Support training

CONCLUSIONS
Appraisee
  Additional comments/information

Appraiser
  Additional comments/information

Review date
Signature of appraisee
Signature of appraiser

Figure 5: *Appraisal list*

This is the opportunity to really assess the **person** and the **needs**. You will have already commented on the weaknesses when they occurred but **this will be the time to assess**:

- what the real problems are
- how they can be corrected
- make a plan of action
- target a review date.

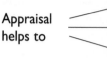

Appraisal
helps to

develop staff

identify their needs

identify your needs

It is also the first line of action for **fair dismissal**. It may become necessary to dismiss a member of staff at a later date if there has been no improvement. Only with a proper initial appraisal will you be able to tell whether performance has improved or not. (See Reference Section, 'Fair Dismissal'.) Appraisal, carried out correctly, is also an excellent exercise for maintaining and improving staff relations and assessing performance objectively.

Refer to the information given, and:
a) prepare an appraisal form for use in your business or salon
b) complete the appraisal form with a colleague, with you taking the supervisory person's role
c) evaluate your appraisal form on its suitability for the task.

In your supervisory role identify the advantages of being able to conduct the appraisals of junior staff rather than your manager.

Explain how you would carry out the appraisal of a member of staff who has recently been repeatedly late and tired at work and whose attitude towards staff and clients has deteriorated.

CHAPTER 3 *Training and development*

Self-development in the supervisory position

Most salons realise the necessity for ongoing training, and a progressive business will consider training as a key factor.

List the main qualities of a supervisory person.

YOU WILL BE RESPONSIBLE FOR **ARRANGING TRAINING OF STAFF,** WHETHER IT BE ONE PERSON OR TEN PEOPLE.

Management will no doubt want to offer **you** the opportunity to improve your existing skills or to develop new ones; they will offer you training where appropriate.

In a large establishment you will probably receive **'in-house' training** (see Champneys interview, pages 45–54) where the training department or personnel section operate regular training courses for all their staff.

In a senior position a training course may take place over a year or even two years so that you receive regular weekly training that is related to your position.

Smaller businesses usually prefer to send their staff to particular training courses to ensure that they keep up to date with the latest professional and technical skills and business techniques.

Whatever method is used, training is vital in order to further self-development.

If the opportunity to train is not freely available then there are numerous courses in Further Education colleges and Adult Education Centres. These can be inexpensive and are designed to meet the changing needs of industry.

You will need to regularly evaluate your own strengths and weaknesses so that you identify your personal requirements in your career development.

Self-development means
- regular evaluation of personal performance
- analyse strengths and weaknesses
- focus on career aims
- achieve short-term targets

Staff training

You should carry out day-to-day training of staff on a one-to-one basis.

One important quality of a supervisor is knowing when to assist, advise and generally offer support to junior staff.

Regular training means staff feel:

- confident and
- competent

and able to cope with their position.

When you decide on a training session:

- it may be because your observations have shown that there is a general weakness in one particular area
- you need to advise your staff of a new development.

So how will you prepare for your session? You will need to decide:

- how long the session will last
- how many people you will train
- what skills you will demonstrate
- how you will demonstrate them
- what visual aids you will need
- what staff participation you will expect
- how you will test/evaluate staff's performance.

If you start with these few points you will be able to develop a plan for training.

Your structure will guide your development. You will then plan each section adequately and not spend too much time on one part.

You will need to consider:

- your voice: this needs to be varied if you want to maintain your staff's attention
- the way you stand: this needs to be a definite presentation of self
- your body language
- your visual language.

Your eyes and body movements are important in conveying your interest in the subject and your audience. Regular movement of the eyes from one person to another sends the message that you are delivering your talk to each person. **Positive** open gestures with your hands or arms suggests warmth and breadth of communication.

A rigid stare, a totally upright, fixed body with no hand movements conveys a closed unfriendly message.

REMEMBER

- your approach
- your enthusiasm
- your tone of voice
- your information

are the tools of your success in delivering a successful training session.

TRAINING STAFF INITIATIVE

You may offer a creative training session developing staff initiative. **Developing staff awareness** in the business environment is vital to success. Staff need to understand the importance of their particular roles in the structure.

CREATIVE PRESENTATION

Mounting and presenting display material requires skill and expertise. The first major point is emphasising the relevance and importance of displays.

You should provide training in display/presentation skills because you can **never** assume that everyone can mount a display.

WHAT DO YOU NEED FOR THIS TYPE OF TRAINING?

- You will need all the material/product that you are going to display. Perhaps you are going to promote a whole new range of:
  - product
  - tee-shirts/leisurewear
  - holdalls
  - cosmetic bags.
- You will require display boards, units and cabinets. Staff will need to know how the display units work: how they join together; safety considerations,

  e.g. no risk of falling, tipping, coming apart.
- Then you will demonstrate different types of display. Will you have a backdrop? A large poster? Picture?
- You will then show how you will mount: a large item such as a leisure shirt; a heavy item such as a holdall.
- You will need to consider: where the product will be placed in relation to other articles; how you will ensure all materials can be seen well. Compare examples of good and poor presentation.

REMEMBER

You must demonstrate all the skills that are necessary for the display so that your trainees know:
- how to mount display units/boards safely
- how to display all sizes of material
- how to develop people's interest in the material
- the relevance of: **interesting**, **informative**, **fresh**, **clean**, **creative**, displays.
- how to make clients: **aware**, **interested**, **keen to buy** the latest products/promotions that the business has to offer.

The success of good training is seen in the product sales.

All this is relevant in training because individuals can develop awareness and initiative and understand the need to:

- **train**
- **monitor sales before and after promotions**

- change materials and displays regularly
- plan effectively to ensure a cost-effective service.

CHAPTER 4 *Selling*

In a supervisory role you will be expected to be experienced in selling and be able to guide and train others. You will probably have a system to record your staff's sales and if not it will be necessary for you to create one. This will help you to:

- **monitor the individual therapist's sales**
- **calculate commission**
- **consider sales techniques in the therapist's appraisal.**

In order to sell effectively the client has got to want the product or service. The client must feel that the service or product is right for him or her.

Knowledgeable staff:

- know their products
- know their services
- can calculate what a client needs.

Staff training for sales

Regular training and incentive schemes form the basis for a good selling environment:

Regular training

Product

Services

Generates more
sales

A junior member of staff needs support training in selling. Give a detailed description of the training session you would present.

Regular product training

- keeps the therapist up to date
- stimulates selling skills.

SERVICES

Learning new services means that the staff can offer a greater variety of treatments.

This means that:

- staff learn new skills and refresh existing ones
- staff have greater job satisfaction.

INCENTIVE SCHEMES

You should monitor **incentive schemes** for your staff. You may be included in this, or management may offer you a different pay structure, an annual bonus or a share of the profits.

Incentive schemes are a good way to:

- promote more sales
- reward staff for their effort.

Staff are generally paid a high commission on sales products and a lower one on services. A high-priced product will earn good sales commission for the employee so that she/he has a good incentive to sell the product.

Many businesses offer incentive schemes, such as a monthly chart recording the individual employee's sales. The winner for the month then receives a bonus or prize. This can be a very good way to gain extra perks and can encourage individuals to perfect their selling skills.

You will need to assess when a scheme needs changing.

REMEMBER

You are working with the other employees:
- **listen** to their comments
- **note** their likes or dislikes
- if the system is not functioning well **note the changes** early
- **adjust the system** if it is your responsibility
- **report** to management with your suggestions for improvement.

Selling practices

When you are supervising the staff in selling you will need to make several observations about **how**:

- the sale is started
- the client's needs are identified
- the therapist responds
- the product or service is sold
- link selling can be encouraged
- the sale is transacted (closed).

Your role is **twofold**:

- **you are supervising a member of staff**
- **you are ensuring the client is satisfied.**

Ask yourself – **did the therapist**:

- smile, look relaxed, look interested, speak confidently
- find out what the client needed
- explain how the product or service would benefit the client
- link the sale to other products or services
- note when the client was considering, thinking, nodding her head (buying signs) and then **wait** patiently
- respond as soon as the client said 'yes'
- process the sale – take payment and record the information on the client's record card or file
- smile and thank the client?

If the therapist missed any of these basic points then further training is needed.

You will need to **offer advice** or set up role play situations so that the therapist can develop *confidence* and *competence*.

CHAPTER 5

The manager and management skills

Good management means that you use all the necessary skills to achieve good results, with the support of your staff team.

THE MANAGER MUST POSSESS A VARIETY OF QUALITIES AND SKILLS:

- good leadership
- good organisational ability
- enthusiasm
- patience
- entrepreneurial skills
- integrity
- responsibility
- initiative
- good communication.

THE MANAGER'S ROLE IS TO:

- plan how the business is run
- carry it out by defining clearly the aims and objectives
- direct operations
- delegate duties and responsibilities
- co-ordinate results
- motivate people
- oversee problems
- counsel staff
- offer all staff praise and encouragement
- be able to evaluate all the areas of work
- train staff.

The manager as organiser

The first major skill is to be able to **prioritise**.

The manager's role can be overwhelming with multiple jobs and it is important that jobs are placed in order of priority.

PLANNING CHARTS

These offer a yearly, monthly or daily planning guide that can help you keep to your plans and advise your staff of your major plans. A **desk diary** will help you record your personal workload with more details of your appointments.

Your work will involve
- meetings
- interviewing staff
- stock control
- training and planning
- business accounts (unless you employ an accountant)
- staff discipline

If you are in a small business you will work closely with your staff and carry out a number of duties yourself.

If you are a manager of a large business you will usually have a supervisory person/line manager to whom you can delegate some of your duties. This person will deal immediately with problems arising

- with staff
- in the salon.

During the day, on a regular basis, you will need to consult with your line manager/supervisor to ensure you are fully aware of the working situation.

Regular meetings ensure that you are well informed and gives you the opportunity to:

- identify areas of concern
- discuss a change of methods
- study resources
- implement new ideas
- measure and evaluate performance.

You will also want to spend some time with your staff so that they are aware that you are involved with 'their' work as well as your work.

Good staff relations and communication are vital if a business is to be successful.

Staff need to know the business structure and what individual staff do. This means that everyone can value their position in the business and see it as an important part of the whole system.

The manager delegates to

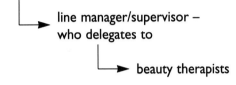

line manager/supervisor – who delegates to

beauty therapists

CHAMPNEYS

Beauty therapists work in a variety of establishments and use numerous skills in their daily tasks. Let us take a look at some of the places where beauty therapists work and see the skills that are necessary in their jobs.

Champneys is an international health resort situated in wooded parkland above the Vale of Aylesbury on the edge of the Chiltern Hills in Buckinghamshire.

Champneys Health Resort is a very large establishment and it is part of the Champneys Group which also includes

- a spa on board the *Oriana*, a cruise ship
- the London Club at Piccadilly
- a spa at Gleneagles Hotel, Scotland
- the International College of Health and Beauty at Tring.

At the resort the **general manager** is assisted by an **executive management team** in the running of the company. **Heads of Department** delegate to **supervisory people** who are responsible for the daily operational work.

Champneys aim to give their resident guests (over 100 daily) a personal health programme in a relaxed, peaceful situation to ensure that the stresses and strains of everyday life are relieved.

Champneys employ a variety of **health consultants** to operate the programme for their guests. They have a large spa where beauty therapy and aromatherapy and a range of other treatments are offered.

The following interviews demonstrate the role of the beauty therapist in this type of establishment and the importance of working as a team in a large business structure.

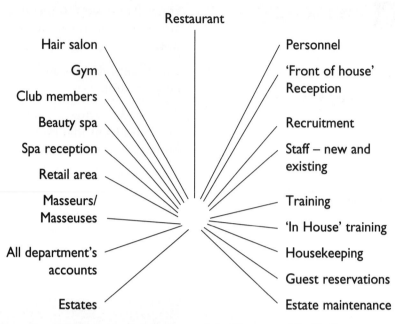

Figure 6:   *All the interrelated aspects of the Champney Health Resort*

INTERVIEW WITH LIZ, SPA MANAGER

Q *How long have you worked at Champneys Liz?*

A Three years. I started as a masseuse. I had been working full-time as a beauty therapist but I enjoyed massage so I applied for the position. More recently I have gained the position of spa manager. I have acquired a lot of experience in my time here. I had been working for about seven years in beauty therapy prior to joining Champneys.

Q *Does management encourage internal promotion?*

A If you have the necessary qualifications and meet the criteria for the position, yes. I would say that they encourage individuals to develop themselves. I have had to make the decision to give up treatments totally and concentrate on management. I am currently being trained in a managerial position, in-house.

Q *What are your responsibilities?*

A My responsibilities are finance and budgeting, recruiting, spa development. I am responsible for all the supervisors in the spa. They supervise their areas and I oversee them. There is a supervisor on duty 24 hours a day to ensure smooth operations.

What are your working hours?

 Generally about 40 hours a week but being in a salaried position you have to be flexible, depending on the needs of the business.

 Are you responsible for training the supervisors?

 I am responsible for training them on the day-to-day duties, the personnel department organises the training in interview skills, appraisal skills and disciplinary skills.

 Are you responsible for discipline of staff?

A If the supervisor on duty feels that there is a situation which requires a verbal warning she will go ahead and give this. Then I am informed, a designated form is completed, and the therapist and the supervisor sign it. It is retained on record for six months.

 What about health and safety legislation; who is responsible for ensuring that this is carried out?

A The supervisor on duty is responsible for checking that health and safety regulations are complied with. It is the individual's responsibility to ensure that they work hygienically and safely.
Fire procedure is also the responsibility of the training supervisor. Management arrange fire practices on a regular basis.

 Are the staff expected to do other duties apart from their designated job?

A Yes, the contract of employment states 'any other reasonable duty'. This would be interpreted as work related.

Q **Do you employ the staff?**

A Yes, I conduct the oral interview. A practical session is conducted by the training supervisor. She knows what is required in the salon. All applicants must have the full beauty therapy skills. We then put them on our own induction training course for a week so that methods are standardised.

Q **Are there any particular qualities that you look for, and is the age of the applicant important?**

A Age is not important but the right qualities are. I will employ people from 19 to 60. I find that older people have often had previous experience in industry as nurses or secretaries and this means that they are very good with the public. Our guests come to be cared for and pampered. We have a wide range of professional people and royalty. The therapist must be able to communicate effectively with all types of people. We need therapists who are:

• discerning

- genuinely friendly
- able to demonstrate good communication skills
- skilful in their job
- full of personality
- able to demonstrate a wide range of life skills.

Quite often the younger therapists find difficulty demonstrating a good knowledge of **life skills**. Their confidence needs to develop.

Our guests expect high standards, excellent treatments, personal care and attention from confident friendly therapists. Our beauty therapists must be able to establish a rapport and extend a listening ear with each guest. They must give excellent service and best advice at all times.

Q *Is there a structure for beauty therapists? What perks go with the job?*

A There are two grades. A therapist will start on Grade 1 and progress to Grade 2 after six to nine months. The therapists are appraised after six to nine months (or once a year). Everyone is paid hourly up to supervisor level. There is no commission on treatments but product companies offer incentives through commission and product vouchers. We give therapists 33 per cent discount on products, additional in-house training, and a birthday treatment. Meals are free when they are on duty and residential facilities are available. They also get 25 per cent off treatments. This has been an excellent training and developmental ground for me and as the company is developing all the time it will allow me to grow with it extending my knowledge and experience.

INTERVIEW WITH TASMAN, SPA RECEPTIONIST (QUALIFIED BEAUTY THERAPIST)

Q *How long have you worked here?*

A Two and a half years, initially as a beauty therapist, but now as spa receptionist. Only qualified beauty therapists can be spa receptionists because they need to fully know and understand beauty therapy treatments. I was trained for this position by my supervisor.

Q *How many spa receptionists are there?*

A There are three of us who work shifts and three floating staff that work fixed hours. We work two shifts early 7.30 am–4.00 pm and late 1.00 pm–9.00 pm. The floating staff work 10.00 am–6.00 pm. There are always two people on the spa reception desk and an additional floater at the specified times. This is a very busy area and needs to be fully staffed.

Q   *What are your duties?*

A   I am responsible for training the spa receptionists on the desk. This takes three weeks. It means I select the beauty therapists to train for this position; not everyone is suitable because the job can be very demanding. They need to have at least one year's experience in the resort and have an outgoing personality. Some therapists prefer to remain giving treatments even if they have the right qualities, as this job can be stressful. The therapists have to be trained in handling bookings, the computerised till, handling queries arising from treatments, the sunbed and mail orders (we are responsible for telephone orders for beauty products). They also open and cash up reception.

We have a training file and when the girls have reached the standard of competence this is marked on the appropriate sheet.

Q   *Do you have duties relating to fire evacuation?*

A   Yes, I must make sure that I take the guest lists and all the treatment lists with me when I leave. The spa supervisor is responsible for locking the till and taking out the computer disks.

I have no responsibility for guests unless they are in the immediate area or the retail area. Then I escort them to the designated area.

Q   *What about guest complaints?*

A   The spa receptionists deal with these as far as possible. Sometimes the query is straightforward but if it is necessary to offer a complimentary treatment we must pass this to the supervisor. We do not have the authority to do this.

Q   *How do your duties differ from those in a beauty salon?*

A   Well, because we have residential clients this means we have to be well informed and this must be an on-going process. We keep a diary and important points or queries are noted. This 'Handover Diary' is given to the next person on duty. Unlike a beauty salon, the beauty therapists do not make detailed client records. The nurse is responsible for checking the client's health and blood pressure when the guest arrives. The guest's medical slip is sent to the therapist before treatment.

The therapist does make out a prescription sheet for skin type and products but this kept for only a limited period because of the vast number of guests.

Do you have any responsibility for disciplinary action over other members of staff?

> **A** No. Any problem with staff must be directed to the supervisor on duty. If she wasn't available then I would take it to the head of spa.

Q ***What about security?***

> **A** We are basically responsible for what is in the till and we must be sure that we lock it at the end of the day and that keys aren't left in the till.
>
> We are also responsible for all the keys of the treatment rooms. The girls hand in the keys at the end of the day's shift. We must make certain that we have all the keys. If any key is missing, we have to go and search for it. We are usually the last to leave. The supervisor will check with the spa receptionist that everything has been done. We must also check that everything (e.g. the sunbeds) is turned off. Everything (e.g. date sheets) must be left ready for the morning shift. Cashing up is obviously very important and it is necessary to have cover on reception at this time to ensure that the spa receptionist is not interrupted. Anyone working would be expected to carry out cover.
>
> Training for this is sometimes necessary to ensure that the person covering knows exactly what to do.
>
> A list of duties could include:

1 check air conditioning and all plugs are turned off
2 turn off sunbeds and air conditioning, prepare room for morning, empty bins, replace bin liners, wipe shelves, change 'goggle' solution, turn off stereo and lights
3 empty bins in and around spa office
4 check cupboards in retail shop are locked
5 tidy displays
6 lock away oils
7 lock cupboards in reception
8 photocopy appointment sheets for the next day
9 change daily events sheet
10 put on name of that day's duty supervisor
11 turn off any electrical items, such as e.g. TV or radio
12 answer the telephone – refer to the supervisor if you require assistance.
13 ensure that tasks have been completed and that the spa receptionist is satisfied.

 Do you have an employment contract?

> **A** Yes. This is very carefully explained so that you are fully aware of its content, including reasons for dismissal. A morning was spent explaining the contract. My supervisor was responsible for this.

Is there a task you do not perform in this area?

A Yes – the rota, dealing with guest complaints, organising cover for absence. These are the supervisor's jobs.

The staff work varied shifts to ensure that the resort is operational. This means that shifts must overlap. Everything is fine but there will always be some absenteeism and this can be demanding for the person completing the rota.

The resort has:

21 beauty therapists who work shifts	9.30–6.00 *or* 1.00–9.00
12 masseuses/masseurs	8.30–1.00
Spa receptionists work	7.30–4.00 *or* 1.00–9.00
and there are some staff who are floaters who work	10.00–6.00

Occasionally temporary staff are employed if there is a staff shortage.

At present the rota is prepared manually but it will soon be computerised.

Q **Do your career plans include the resort?**

A No, not really now. I have gained a lot of experience in this position and working here has been good, but I would like to start teaching full-time. I already teach part-time at a local college.

INTERVIEW WITH SHARON, (BEAUTY THERAPIST) SALES CONSULTANT, MAKE-UP ARTIST

Q **I understand that you trained in the Champneys School of Beauty Therapy which is attached to the resort. Did you come here to work straightaway?**

A No, that was six years ago. I worked in salons in Hertfordshire and I worked in Tenerife for a year. I was made redundant on two occasions, and I was working for myself when I saw an advertisement for sales work here.

Q **What made you decide to move into selling?**

 I have always enjoyed selling and wanted to do this full-time. I enjoy make-up as well and took every opportunity to further this skill. I entered the National Bride of the Year Make-up Competition in 1990.

At my interview I realised that the job was all selling and make-up and

I was pleased to get the position. My job description was to:

- promote the beauty shop
- develop skincare and homecare for our clientele.

 Do you work alone?

 There are two of us and we work 9 am–5.30 pm five days a week with alternate weekends off.

Who is your supervisor?

 Kelly, the reception supervisor.

What sort of things do you do?

We have a spacious product-filled beauty shop and we give the house guests a personal face and body plan. This may include a make-up. We give one-to-one attention. I plan weekly talks on beauty which are given in the Drawing Room of the resort. This often includes a make-up demonstration.

We are also responsible for all the ordering of stock. We prepare this and finally the spa manager approves the order. We must check the delivery note, and the invoice, and ensure that everything is correct. This is very important. We hold a large stock because we sell a lot of products.

 How many product ranges do you stock?

 Four.

 Do you receive product training?

Yes, very regularly. We also get training from the product company on positive thinking and attitude, which is selling related.

 Do you have monthly targets?

We have weekly targets, at present £4,000 a week without VAT. We receive 1% commission on and above this amount. The product companies also give us good incentives in vouchers or products.

 Are you responsible for all the money transactions?

 No, reception deals with all the money transactions.

Q *What about Health and Safety legislation?*

 A We are given clear instructions on our duties in relation to this and to fire procedure. It is our duty to make sure that we carry out the instructions. All the beauty staff have regular weekly meetings where we can discuss any points and where information is given to us.

Q *What are your future plans?*

 A I would like to be an area manager for a product company. This is my next goal.

INTERVIEW WITH LORNA, (BEAUTY THERAPIST) MASSEUSE

 Q *How long have you worked at Champneys?*

 A Two years. Before that I worked in a beauty salon in Buckinghamshire for a year. I came here as a beauty therapist but after a year I changed to massage only. I have always preferred massage and this really suits me.

 Q *Who is your supervisor?*

 A I am responsible to Colin, who is the massage administrator.

 Q *What are your working hours?*

A I work 8.30 am–1.00 pm six mornings a week and every six weeks we can take an unpaid Saturday. We receive a higher hourly rate than the beauty therapists.

Q *Do you have specific duties?*

A I must keep my treatment room tidy. We don't have client records to maintain but we do have medical slips which are given to us by the medical sister who deals with guests as they arrive at the resort. Any relevant information is recorded on the slip and any necessary information can be put on the client's history which is stored on computer.

If we are free we are expected to assist in treatment room reception. This means we:

- check the daily guest record sheet
- check guests in the rest area
- assist with salt rubs.

I am expected to 'lend a hand' if I am not taking a break.

 Q *What happens in the event of fire breaking out?*

 A I must take my client (clothed in towels) to the designated area. We are only responsible for our immediate client.

Q *Are there any promotional prospects open to you?*

A I could become a trainer in massage (in-house training). This would be an extra responsibility rather than a financial promotion. At the moment I enjoy my work and I have no immediate plans.

PART 2 *Effective client relationships*

CHAPTER 6   *Client handling*

The discerning client expects a lot from the beauty therapist. There are often many salons for her to choose from so she can afford to be selective.

Initially the enquirer may make a telephone enquiry. How her call is dealt with will often determine whether she becomes a client.

What will she expect when she rings?

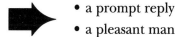

- a prompt reply
- a pleasant manner
- accurate knowledgeable information (length of treatment, cost . . .)
- an appointment

If a receptionist is employed to answer telephone calls (see interview, pages 48–51) it is vital that she has a knowledge of the salon treatments. If she/he is unable to answer the enquirers' questions it is important that there is someone who can offer the expertise. This information needs to be given promptly. It is never good practice to keep a client waiting on the telephone. This creates the impression that the establishment is not properly managed.

REMEMBER

- your enquirer cannot see you, she has only your voice as communication.

Ensure that your telephone service is:

- prompt
- pleasant
- professional

and that your information is:

- accurate
- relevant
- understood.

If your enquirer makes an appointment, record it carefully and accurately on the appropriate page of the appointment book – mistakes often occur at this early stage. Ensure that adequate time has been allocated for consultation and treatment.

Role play a telephone enquiry explaining to a new client:
a) a warm wax (leg treatment)

b) the duration of the treatment
c) why the client should not have a sauna session before the leg wax.

How did your client select your salon?

Your client arrives for her first treatment. At this stage you may not know whether she/he has had treatments before.

• Is it her/his first visit to a salon?

• Is she/he bewildered or unsure?

• Does she/he know what to expect?

On the other hand she/he may have received many treatments in a variety of places and have a wealth of experience.

Why has the prospective client come for treatment?

• special treat – birthday, anniversary

• received a gift voucher

• to look younger

• to slim and control weight

• problem skin

• relaxation and stress relief

Whatever your prospective client's reasons for coming to the establishment are, **the most important point is that you are there to attend to her/his individual needs**.

Make the most of this opportunity of presenting yourself as a true professional.

Design a questionnaire to ask new and existing clients why they selected the salon, what are their likes and dislikes, and what suggestions they might have to improve the salon/services.

How will you greet your client?

You will:

- make her/him feel welcome
- greet her/him sincerely/courteously
- treat her/him with respect
- show a genuine interest.

Effective client liaison is achieved by being sincere and **genuinely** enjoying meeting your client. Artificial smiles and gushing greetings do not make the client feel confident.

A relaxed, gentle approach will allow the client to feel assured and welcome in the salon environment.

The importance of the therapist's appearance has already been explained but it cannot be emphasised too much. The client wants to see a clean well-presented professional beauty therapist.

The client should be taken to a private room/cubicle area where she/he can talk without being overheard.

Cost effectiveness

Any salon or sole operator must consider cost effectiveness if a business is to succeed. The operator must be aware of business overheads, staff salaries and the cost per hour of operating the business.

- This means that preparation for treatments and tidying, sterilisation and generally necessary routine tasks have been built in to the costing.

BUT, time should **never** be skimped with the client so that she/he feels rushed, unprepared or dissatisfied. When your client books an appointment the time allocated to the treatment is exclusively for the client.

REMEMBER

the client is paying for
- your skill/expertise
- your client handling skills.

When the treatment is finished the client must be made aware, gently but firmly, that you have other clients to follow, and that her/his treatment time has ended for that day.

This will ensure that clients who enjoy talking (and talking) do not overstay and make you rush, or be late for your next appointment.

Learning to handle your clients skilfully and advising them correctly so that they are fully aware of your working situation is all part of your skill development.

As a supervisor prepare a role play training to show therapists how to communicate effectively with two different client types

e.g.
a) a client is quiet, appears apprehensive
b) a client disagrees with her treatment cost.

CHAPTER 7

Client consultation

The **client consultation** is of paramount importance. Increasingly we are aware of the significance of studying the whole person in order to be able to offer the best advice and ultimately the most appropriate treatments.

This means that sufficient time must be allowed for the consultation to be conducted. If it is the client's first appointment, this must be taken into account at the time of booking the appointment.

Sometimes a client will choose to come for a consultation first and book the treatment on a different day. This can be a good idea, as it can show contra-indications for a particular treatment. The consultation is your key to successful business. It serves several vital purposes:

- the opportunity to **meet, welcome** and get to know your client – to establish good communication
- the chance to **listen** to the client's needs
- the ability to **establish the client's needs** and assess her/his suitability for treatment and to record relevant details
- the opportunity to **explain** the treatments available
- the opportunity to **demonstrate** your professional expertise by explaining treatments **in language that the client understands**
- the scope to design **a personal treatment plan** for the client and, on her/his agreement, to confirm the sale.

Points to note

Develop your communication skills:

- listen to your client
- talk with your client
- remember vital information
- try not to write, head down, all the time you are recording information

- look at your client, note a few points at a time
- be interested, be attentive
- ALWAYS GIVE THE BEST ADVICE.

REMEMBER

- **take it slowly**
- check your client **understands** the benefit.

You are establishing a firm sale and meeting your client's needs. Your sales skills will develop automatically if your treatments are based on the client's needs.

- The client must **need**.
- You must explain the treatments and **benefits**.
- The sale of treatment is **confirmed**.

The **satisfied** client returns again and again.

List the key points of a client consultation and say what they mean to you.

How will you record basic information?

Use a **record card**.

REMEMBER

- The record card is a source of information for you and any other therapist to refer to for subsequent treatments

You must

- write clearly
- record vital facts

You will want the client to understand the importance of recording the information. The client may not wish to tell you all their personal details.

You must use your skill and expertise to explain to the client fully the necessity for accurate records. You must emphasise that everything is confidential and that this just ensures that the best treatment is given. You must also be aware that the client has the right to see everything you record. Some records are a two card system. Personal details are recorded on one and the second is for treatment details.

BEAUTY RECORD CARD

Name:... Age:................................ Tel. No.:..

Address: ....

PERSONAL DOCTOR	DETAILS OF PRESCRIBED DRUGS
Name:	
Address:	
Telephone No.:	

MEDICAL HISTORY

Height: Weight: Chest: Waist: Hips:

Heart Disease: Yes/No   Varicose Veins: Yes/No

Details of Operations: _____

_____

_____

Other Comments: _____

_____

_____

Date	Treatment	Remarks

Figure 7:   *Beauty record card*

THIS SHOWS THE

frequency of treatments
↓
type of treatment
↓
products purchased with treatments

ALL THIS INFORMATION IS IMPORTANT FOR YOU TO

identify your client's progress
↓
record sales of treatment and products

How you ask the question determines how the client answers.

Direct questions usually require short concise answers, e.g. are you taking any medication?

Open questions allow the client to explain more fully, e.g. tell me about your skin problem.

Clients may be quiet, nervous, shy. They will need encouragement to give the answers you need. Some clients are assertive, dominant and direct – they will need a calm, firm approach so that they know you are fully in control of the consultation.

As the consultation develops you will no doubt start to be aware of some of your client's needs. Sometimes the client has a particular problem which she/he will disclose on another visit, such as superfluous hair in a sensitive region.

REMEMBER

• Always question carefully – there may be some very delicate areas that the client doesn't wish to discuss at this stage.

Sometimes clients do not give you the true facts – they tell you what they think you **ought** to know. To engage their trust takes time and expertise, and shows the importance of establishing a good rapport and confidence.

Try to record all the client's needs.

She/he may start by requesting facial treatments but consider body treatments for a later date.

Often a client will reveal a number of problems which could be related to:

- post-pregnancy
- post-hysterectomy
- post-mastectomy

see pages 204–211 for fuller detail.

Your skill and knowledge in the wide range of life skills is vital.

- The client **explains**
- the therapist **empathises** and the best treatment plan is **estabished**.

Good listening skills

The therapist must always **listen** to the client. It is so easy to talk and not to listen.

In the early stages it is quite an achievement if your client wants to talk freely to you.

A general 'picture' of your client can be gained by the information she/he tells you and you will:

- understand more quickly
- be able to assess the client's needs.

You will already have made a number of observations about your client which will help you in your physical assessment.

When your client arrived you will have observed:

- how she/he walked
- how she/he stood
- how she/he sat
- if she/he had any difficulty with mobility.

Body language conveys how a client is feeling, watch:

- eyes
- hand movements
- smile
- mannerisms.

THE MORE YOU READ YOUR CLIENT'S BODY LANGUAGE THE QUICKER YOU
WILL PERCEIVE HER/HIS NEEDS

REMEMBER

• Your client will also be noting your body language

You will have checked for all the major contra-indications before
you proceed.

If your client has a temporary disorder or disease then you must
stop at this stage and advise her to make another appointment
when the problem has gone.

If this is handled properly the client will understand that this is in
her best interests and she will trust your advice. This is the
beginning of establishing a rapport built on professional skill and
expertise.

Explain, in language a client can understand, the
importance of a detailed consultation before
planning a course of mechanical massage to
assist with a cellulite problem on the thighs and
buttocks.

Recording personal details

It has already been mentioned that it is necessary to explain to
your client the importance of recording personal details on the
record card. If this is explained correctly to the client, the client
views this as important and not as an invasion of privacy. Clients
usually appreciate the time and attention that they receive.

Salon treatments offer such a wide variety of beauty and holistic
treatments today that it is necessary to consider a **much wider
range of questions** to ask the client. Time spent recording this
detail can be beneficial as it presents a full picture of your client
which assists in selecting the best treatments.

Many sales companies produce standard record cards to record
client information. Sometimes these are adequate, but often they
have insufficient space.

Many salons have client folders and produce their own forms so
that more detailed information can be recorded.

Some salons store the information on computer (see Reference
Section page 251)

You will need to record personal information as shown in figure 8.

PERSONAL DETAILS

name . . . .

address . . . .

telephone number . . . .

doctor's name and address . . . .

height . . . .

weight . . . .

age group . . . .

marital status . . . .

children . . . .

general health . . . .

recent operations . . . .

MEDICAL HISTORY (* delete as appropriate)

Circulatory conditions
  * high blood pressure
  * low blood pressure
  * angina
  * thrombosis
  * varicose veins
  * other

Respiratory conditions
  * asthma
  * hayfever
  * bronchitis
  * sinusitis
  * other

Neurological conditions
  * epilepsy
  * paralysis
  * nervous tension
  * neuralgia
  * other

Digestive conditions
  * constipation
  * diarrhoea
  * hiatus hernia
  * gallstones
  * other

Skeletal conditions
  * fractures
  * kyphosis
  * scoliosis
  * lordosis
  * osteoarthritis
  * other

Renal/urinary conditions
  * kidney infections
  * kidney stones
  * urinary infections
  * cystitis
  * fluid retention
  * other

Endocrine conditions
  * exophthalmic goitre
  * Cushing's syndrome
  * diabetes
  * abnormal hair growth
  * other

Gynaecological conditions
  * menopause
  * pregnancy
  * ovarian cyst
  * pre-menstrual tension
  * other

Muscular conditions
  * fibrositis
  * torticollis
  * cramp
  * other

Medication
  * contraceptive pill
  * high blood pressure pills
  * other

Hereditary conditions
  * circulatory disorders
  * abnormal hair growth
  * other

Diet
  * varied and balanced diet
  * regular meals/snacks
  * protein
  * carbohydrate
  * fat – high animal
      – high dairy
  * vegetables/fruit
  * fluid intake
  * water intake
  * alcohol
  * sugar
  * vegetarian

LIFESTYLE
Work
  * active
  * sedentary
  * environment

Relaxation
  * exercise pattern
  * hobbies

Habits
  * smoker
  * drinker
  * other

Emotional problems
  * depression
  * other

Stress level
  * scale low 1–10 high
  * possible causes

Sleep pattern
  * constant
  * disturbed
  * insomnia

ANY OTHER INFORMATION
. . . .

COMMENTS
. . . .

SKIN ANALYSIS
  * texture
  * colour
  * tone/elasticity
  * blemishes
  * broken capillaries
  * dehydration
  * wrinkles
  * comedones
  * pigmentation
  * scarred
  * sun-damaged
  * congested
  * inflamed
  * reactive– heat
          – cold
  * healing time

Skin abnormalities
  * congenital
  * acquired

Skin type
  * normal
  * oily
  * dry
  * combination
  * sensitive
  * problem
  * young
  * mature
  * other

Homecare routine
  * products used

Skin disorders
  * acne vulgaris
  * acna rosacea
  * dermatitis
  * eczema
  * urticaria
  * skin cancer
  * herpes simplex
  * psoriasis
  * other

Allergies
  * food
  * environment
  * medication
  * other

EPILATION ANALYSIS
(in conjunction with earlier information)
Previous epilation. . . . .
Previous results . . . .
Hair growth history
  * since puberty
Hair growth situation
  * chin
  * lip
  * neck
  * eyebrows
  * other
Hair growth type
  * dense
  * fine
  * strong

Figure 8:   *A detailed list of what to record*

Client complaints

As a supervisory person you will need to give your staff:

- advice
- training

on how to deal with complaints.

This can be difficult for new or inexperienced members of staff.

They must learn to deal with complaints as they occur in the salon. However, you or a senior person should always be available for support.

You may draw up a code of practice such as this:

- always remain calm
- take the client to a quiet area
- offer her/him a seat
- ask the client to explain the problem (complaint)
- listen
- show interest in your client and be understanding and diplomatic
- if the client is being difficult you need supervisory assistance
- if the client is being reasonable you may offer a solution
- you will need to consult with the supervisor if you are offering a refund or alternative treatment.

REMEMBER

- stay calm
- never get angry
- there is always someone to help you.

Give examples of direct questions and open questions when conducting a client consultation. Explain when open questions are necessary and why direct questions could be a definite disadvantage.

CHAPTER 8

Conducting a physical assessment

Your client is going to have a **physical assessment** before her body treatment.

Figure assessment cards show most of the vital information that needs to be recorded.

BODY TREATMENT CARD				NAME:					
ADDRESS:						TEL: Work 　　　Home			
DOCTOR:			MEDICATION			SMOKE	DRINK		AGE
MEDICAL HISTORY	Number of Pregnancies		Ages of Children			Recent Post-Natal Examination			
OPERATIONS	Hysterectomy	Date	Caesarean Section	Date					
GENERAL HEALTH	Good	Poor	Constipation	High Blood Pressure		Varicose Veins			
BODY CONDITION	Overweight	Poor Muscle Tone	Underweight	Out of Proportion					

TREATMENT PLAN	General Reduction	Specific Reduction	Treatments Booked											
	Massage & Relaxation	Cellulite	Treatments Completed	1	2	3	4	5	6	7	8	9	10	

	DATE	TREATMENT	PRODUCTS AND HOME CARE ADVICE
1			
2			
3			
4			
5			
6			
7			
8			
9			
10			

BODY TREATMENT CARD | NAME:

DIET PLAN SUGGESTION		HEIGHT:

DIET PLAN SUGGESTION	
MODERATE PROTEIN/LOW CARBOHYDRATE	
MOD. PROTEIN/LOW FAT/LOW CARBOHYDRATE	
ELIMINATION DIET	
CARBOHYDRATE UNIT DIET	

	TREATMENT	1st	2nd	3rd	4th	5th	6th	7th	8th	9th	10th
	DATE:										
	WEIGHT										
1	BUST/CHEST										
2	WAIST										
3	HIPS										
4	UPPER THIGH L										
	UPPER THIGH R										
5	MID THIGH L										
	MID THIGH R										
6	KNEE										
7	CALF										
8	ANKLE										
9	WRIST										
10	UPPER ARM L										
	UPPER ARM R										

FIGURE & POSTURE NOTES

Rounded Shoulders		Abdominal Weakness		Cellulite on Thighs	
Spinal Curvature		Weak Inside Thighs		Adipose Deposit on Buttocks	
Tension in Upper Back		Fluid on Knees		Heavy Lower Legs	

EXERCISE PLAN

Figure 9:
Body treatment card

But how will you handle your client?

Initially you will have made some assessment of figure type through her/his clothing. Then she/he must remove her/his clothes except for underwear.

Make sure that

- she/he has a place to change
- a suitable gown is provided
- the client is comfortable

As you proceed ensure that your client is aware and understands what you are doing:

- your skilful, **simple** explanation reassures the client of good technical knowledge and enables her/him to trust you.

REMEMBER

- always be positive.

Explain the benefits of:

- knowing

- understanding
- corrective techniques.

Never show

- shock
- alarm
- concern.

Some clients can become alarmed very quickly. If something appears to be wrong, e.g. if a mole that you observe is not as it should be, you may suggest your client checks with the doctor.

REMEMBER

- beauty therapists are often the first people to see a disorder – your suggestion may save distress later.

YOU MUST ALWAYS BE VERY AWARE OF YOUR CLIENT AND NEVER UNDERESTIMATE HOW SHE/HE WILL REACT.

When the assessment is complete you will want to discuss the main points with your client. It may affect your intended treatment plan. You will want the client to fully understand the initial treatment and subsequent treatments.

You will possibly want your client to understand other factors which can influence the treatment, such as diet, exercise, lifestyle. Before you give body treatments you must consider the client's:

- body type
- posture
- possible skeletal disorders
- possible figure problems.

In order to correctly assess your client's needs you will need to make certain observations.

How you do this is important.

Your client doesn't want to be told that she has:

- 'a crooked back'
- 'fat hips'
- 'heavy legs'.

She needs to understand that we are all **individuals** and our bodies reflect certain **hereditary tendencies** as well as postural problems due to our working environment.

The client needs to understand that we each have our own characteristics and you are assessing her/his to enable you to design the most effective course of treatment.

Your client will then look forward to the figure analysis and appreciate the time that you take to assess her/his needs.

Explain why it is important to consider the client's body type and any hereditary features when considering a weight reducing programme.

Postural faults and figure faults can be explained as you observe them.

Assessment of

- superfluous body fat
- poor muscle tone
- cellulite

can be observed and at the same time the most appropriate treatment can be discussed.

When you assess the client's posture you will want to explain the **benefits of good posture**. The client will want to know why it is important and why it's worth changing or adjusting posture.

Good posture means:

- increased energy when muscles are balanced
- better breathing (chest is not contracted)
- more efficient digestion (digestive organs are not compressed)
- postural problems won't occur if bones are aligned correctly
- the figure functions well and looks good when posture is correct.

For more information see page 215 in the Reference Section.

If you do assist your client in her/his total development she/he must understand the benefits of:

- good posture
- the importance of figure correction.

Correct (good) posture means
|
toned muscles
|
even distribution of weight on
legs and feet

One of your staff has a particular postural problem, which affects how she stands, sits and works. How can you assist the member of staff to ensure that she works safely, fully understands the problem and receives your support to help the condition?

What you should do

All consultations require:

- record of contra-indications
- treatment plan
- follow up
- record of session
- homecare routine
- suggestions
- any other information
- client consent
- therapist's signature.

Your skill in establishing a good rapport with your client shows effective communication. A relaxed, happy client feels at ease to select and buy the treatments she wants.

After careful, knowledgeable consultation your client will be able to enjoy the treatments that will be most beneficial.

REMEMBER

 always check the client fully understands

- the treatment
- the benefits
- the cost
- the treatment plan.

After taking a detailed consultation you find that your client is suffering from stress and is physically and mentally fatigued. Explain to her/him the proposed treatment plan, the frequency and the cost, and any other suggestions you might make.

CHAPTER 9 # *Two interviews with clients*

1. A MIDDLE-AGED CLIENT DESCRIBES A BEAUTY THERAPIST'S ATTITUDE, APPROACH AND GENERAL MANNER

I think that the first impression is very important. I want the therapist to be confident, understanding and put me at ease. I don't want to be made to feel that I have left everything too late.

Personally, I prefer a female therapist, at least in her middle twenties, with a few year's experience. I don't want a 'dolly-bird' who looks great and treats others in a patronising way because she thinks she looks better.

I like to be able to discuss all types of problems to do with the body, but not personal or family problems until I get to know the therapist, after a few years.

I like to talk about weight and diet and skin problems. And I wanted to know all sort of things about the menopause when I reached that stage.

I like the therapist to make me feel relaxed and comfortable in a pleasant, quiet atmosphere and I like her to be genuinely friendly and caring.

2. RENA 'MY IDEA OF A THERAPIST'

What I want from a therapist is someone to be understanding and listen to my moans and groans about the week. I can't stand giggly girls.

Usually I carry on about work and pressure and stress and the boyfriend or lack of one and then I 'zonk' out and go to sleep. I always wake up feeling great.

The massage and facial do my body good and the prattling on does my soul good.

Words of encouragement to start the next week help and booking my next appointment reminds me that I need this unwinding session.

INTERVIEW WITH SALLY, BEAUTY THERAPIST ON A CRUISE LINER

 What made you want to work on liners?

 I wanted to see the world and thought that this would be a good way to do it, as I could carry on working as a beauty therapist at the same time.

 Did you find it difficult to get this position?

 No, I applied to one of the companies I knew employed beauty therapists on boats; that was Coiffeur Transocean (Steiners and Alders are other companies and I believe they have taken over Coiffeur Transocean). I was interviewed and I was given the job. I had previously worked for a few years in local salons in Buckinghamshire.

 Did you have a contract of employment?

 Yes, my contract was for nine months and my pay was tax free, as I was out of the country.

 Was the work varied?

Yes, I covered the whole range of beauty treatments but there was a predominance of massage. I used to do at least twelve massages a day and these were mainly men. I worked shifts and it was always very busy. It is not a job for the work-shy. It was busy at sea and busy in port, but there were perks. I had free accommodation, free meals and travel.

 Were there many beauty therapy staff?

No, considering the liner had twelve hundred passengers. There was one masseur, one hair stylist and me, and there was a manager in charge of the salon. We were responsible to him and he was responsible to the hotel (liner) director.

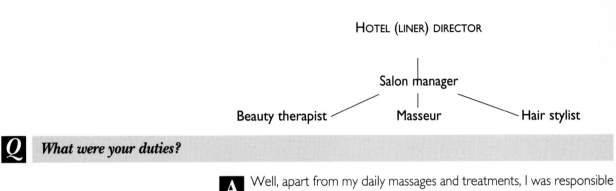

Q *What were your duties?*

A Well, apart from my daily massages and treatments, I was responsible for all the stock, paperwork and in fact everything that had to be done. This went directly to the manager.

Q *Did you like the working environment?*

A Yes, I enjoyed the situation but the work is arduous. One needs to be fit. You are given a lot of responsibility and the smooth running of the salon rests with you. Time is important. You need to be a **good communicator** and have **lots of personality**.

PART 3 *Specialist therapy treatments*

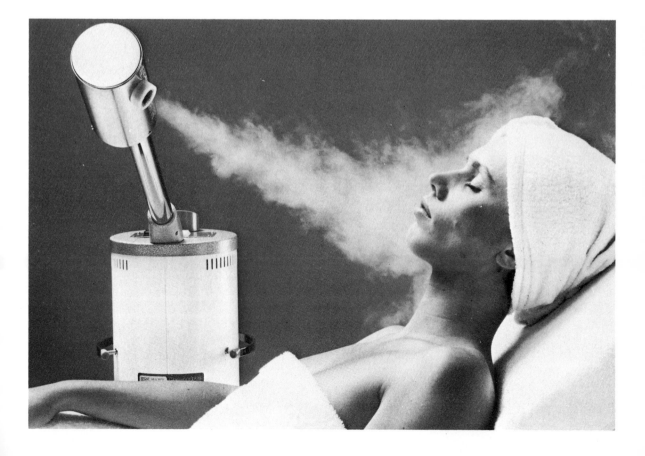

CHAPTER 10

Body massage

Prepare the individual for general therapy sessions and aftercare in particular:

- body massage
- sauna session
- steam session
- hydrotherapy
- spa pool
- suntanning equipment
- infra-red
- before and after care.

The beauty therapist must ensure that the working environment is ready. This means that:

- the treatment room is at a suitable temperature to maintain client comfort throughout the treatment (refer pages 244 and 249, Health and Safety at Work Act 1974, Offices, Shops and Railway Premises Act 1963)
- the room is well-ventilated and clean
- the massage support is hygienically prepared with paper towelling on top of towels and blankets, and additional towels available
- the support is set at the correct height for effective treatment
- the room should be private and quiet so as to present a calm, relaxing atmosphere
- necessary equipment should be clean (sterilised if necessary) and placed on a trolley
- materials required such as talcum powder, oils, moisturising lotion should be placed hygienically on the trolley
- a receptacle for waste should be at hand.

The salon owner has set you a task. There is a small room two and a half metres square in the existing salon which needs to be productive if the salon is to be cost effective.

At present there is no sauna or steam bath. The showers are next door to the room. A sauna seems to be an idea worth developing.

Consider what's available – obtain catalogues.

- Will you have a steam cabinet, or an individual sauna cabinet (can you have both?)

- What other pieces of furniture/equipment will you require in the room?
- What other factors must you consider?

The salon's finances are quite good at the moment but you will still want to be moderate in your purchases.

Detail how you will plan, purchase, and finish this task, for presentation to your employer.

Appearance

The therapist's personal appearance and preparation for work must be considered:

- a clean ironed overall should be worn with a tabard for added protection and hygiene during the treatment
- hair should be tied back off the face
- comfortable, low-heeled shoes should be worn
- jewellery should be limited to a plain wedding band (any other jewellery should be unobtrusive)
- cuts should be hygienically covered with suitable waterproof dressings
- the therapist should consider personal hygiene at all times and, in particular, the washing of hands before and immediately after treatment.

The therapist will have completed a full consultation and recorded all the necessary detail that is required before treatment (see Chapter 6 for details on full consultation).

The therapist must then consider her client.

Is the client

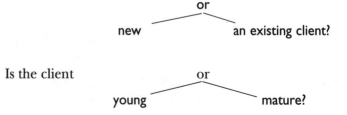

If the client is new, whether she/he is young or mature it is vital that the therapist takes time to put her/him at ease if the client is to gain maximum benefit from the treatment.

Physical relaxation will go hand in hand with **emotional relaxation**, assured comfort and professional expertise.

If the client is an existing one she/he will expect the same high standards that have been **demonstrated** on previous occasions.

The therapist should ensure that she/he is not interrupted once the client has been taken to the room or cubicle where treatment will take place. The client must know that privacy is assured.

The therapist should then explain the procedure to the client so that she/he understands the treatment routine and its benefits.

Many clients feel bewildered if it is their first treatment and they may not relax sufficiently to gain maximum benefit from the session.

Wearing a suitable uniform or overall is important whilst working as a therapist
a) Explain why.
b) What type of material is best?
c) Explain why you think tabards are necessary.
d) Cost uniforms/overalls by writing to at least three manufacturers.

Client preparation

The client, even if she/he is a regular, will usually wait for the therapist's instruction to 'get changed'. The regular client will probably know what to do but should still be directed; the new client will certainly want advice.

Give advice and instructions clearly:

- say what you want them to take off and explain why
- provide a clean gown that fits and disposable paper slippers for hygiene and comfort
- give advice regarding the client's hair, particularly if it is long and loose; it will need securing and protecting during massage
- provide the client with a suitable band or light cap to protect hair, or a disposable cap
- give advice regarding jewellery and personal items and the safe-keeping of these.

Once your client has been advised leave her/him to change in private.

When your client is ready and the personal belongings have been attended to assist her/him in getting on to the massage support and check that the client is comfortable.

Aftercare

It is always pleasant for the client to relax a while before getting up. You will need to wash your hands and complete the client's consultation records. This can be a convenient time to do so.

REMEMBER

- Always advise your client that you are going so that she/he may relax for a few more minutes

The client is then able to relax and enjoy the last beneficial moments of the treatment knowing where you have gone and when you are returning and what she/he is expected to do.

- **Finally** – allow your client **privacy** to dress.

It is always desirable in a salon if the client can sit in a relaxing area, perhaps have a drink and arrange her/his next appointment.

Client comment – massage

INTERVIEW WITH ANN

Q **Can you tell me about your massage treatment Ann?**

A I don't think I really got the best out of it. It was a large establishment and at first I felt very rushed. I was clothed in towels but no one really explained the massage. I lay there quite tense waiting to be told to turn over, lift my head.

Some of the movements were quite hard and hurt. It's very awkward when you don't know what to expect because you don't know if it's normal or not. I felt pleased when it was over. Then I was left alone for about ten minutes. I didn't know whether to get up, get changed, or what.

It would have been nice to have been told:

- what to expect
- what to do
- what was happening at the end.

Did this experience discourage you with other beauty treatments?

A Yes, until now (three years later) I haven't even thought about any treatment.

This must be a constant reminder to any working therapist how important clients are.

ALWAYS REMEMBER THE CLIENT COMES FIRST

Check he/she knows

understands – and

enjoys her/his treatment

Client satisfaction is the key to success:

NO CLIENTS = NO BUSINESS.

Particular massage techniques

(Also, see page 88)

THE ELDERLY CLIENT

 This client may need more particular attention.

REMEMBER

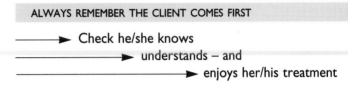

elderly clients can
↓
have hearing loss
↓
have sight loss
↓
be more frail
↓
have difficulty with mobility
↓
bruise more easily
↓
feel the cold

These points must be given consideration:

- in your consultation
- during preparation of the client
- during the massage
- at the end of the treatment.

You must ensure that your client does hear and understand you and that she can see clearly if she needs to write her name. Getting on and off a massage support requires mobile joints even if the support height seems correct for your client.

ALWAYS BE PATIENT AND ASSIST YOUR CLIENT, IF SHE/HE REQUIRES HELP.

Always be particularly attentive to your client's physical well-being during treatment.

Ask yourself:

- have adequate pillows been supplied to support head and limbs?
- have enough towels/blankets been used to maintain a suitable body temperature?

Remember, your **touch** is important.

Always check your client is comfortable and that the movements are pleasant

not too **heavy**
not too **light**

- **Make sure your hands are warm.**

Ensure that the client has the correct medium or lubricant for the treatment, e.g. oil, talcum powder.

The massage techniques should suit the client's bodily needs; that means the rhythm and pressures should be correct for the client's weight and tissue density (see page 88 for massage techniques).

The necessary verbal communication should take place **during treatment** so that the client's needs are noted.

Your client will relax and receive maximum benefit from the massage if you have taken time to establish a rapport and if you understand your client's needs.

At the end of the massage you will want to check that the client has enjoyed the treatment. You will also want to make recommendations for subsequent treatments.

You may want to consider or add to suggestions that you made during the consultation and revise any treatment plan e.g.

postural exercises that the client can do at home to assist a particular part of the body.

EFFICIENT AFTERCARE ENSURES YOUR CLIENT'S TREATMENT IS COMPLETE.

REMEMBER

• successful businesses are built on satisfied clients.

A middle-aged client who suffers with rheumatism feels that she can benefit from various body treatments.
a) Design a three-month programme of treatments.

b) Consider homecare/advice.
c) Explain how you might adjust the programme.

MASSAGE AFTER ILLNESS, AFTER PREGNANCY

The techniques required are those that stimulate the muscles:

• deep effleurage (see over page)
• kneading (deep movement on soft tissue with no bone immediately beneath it)
• tapotement (see over page)

Muscles are often slack due to lack of exercise or poor elasticity. Other massage techniques can be added as the muscles respond.

MASSAGE FOR MUSCULAR TENSION

A **pre-treatment of heat** is often beneficial before this massage. It will help to reduce pain (see heat treatments page 114) and prepare the muscles for massage.

Massage techniques are:

• light effleurage
• deep effleurage
• deep kneading.

It is important to treat the entire body to **stimulate the circulation** and then to carry out **localised massage** where the muscles require attention.

Alternated effleurage ensures that the muscles are relaxed and the massage comfortable.

MASSAGE FOR JOINT MOBILITY

After a general massage to loosen muscles and create suppleness, massage techniques to assist joint mobility include kneading performed with the finger and thumb.

This should always be followed by **effleurage** to ensure that the circulation is stimulated.

Points to consider

MASSAGE OBJECTIVES

- relaxation
- lymphatic drainage (increases the movement of lymph through the superficial lymph vessels)

FORMS OF MASSAGE TECHNIQUES

- effleurage (flowing, stroking movement mainly performed with the flat of the hand)
- petrissage (movement performed with the ball of the fingers and thumbs on soft tissue over bone)
- tapotement (a quick, light vibratory movement of the fingertips)
- vibration (a movement like fine trembling, usually performed with the fingers)

MEDIUM/LUBRICANTS

- oil
- cream
- talcum powder

CONSIDER THE CLIENT TYPE

- nervous
- young
- mature
- elderly
- sedentary
- active
- new
- existing

Contra-indications

These usually make it necessay that the client obtains medical approval.

- **high temperature/fever/infectious diseases**
- **any condition requiring medical treatment**
  - circulatory disorders
  - high blood pressure
  - low blood pressure
  - history of thrombosis
  - embolism
  - epilepsy
  - diabetes
  - malfunction of the nervous system
  - skin disorders
  - severe bruising
  - swellings
  - recent haemorrhage
  - moles/warts
  - recent scar tissue
  - areas showing loss of sensitivity to touch
  - pregnancy – abdominal area in particular
  - cuts/abrasions
  - recent operations
  - recent fractures or sprains
  - metal plates/pins in bone
  - electronic implants
  - heart valve dysfunction
  - 'severe' allergic reaction

CHAPTER 11

Mechanical (gyratory – G5) massage

The gyratory massager works on two planes

vertical – up and down
horizontal – circular

These are unlike vibratory treatments such as vibratory belt machines or some hand-held appliances which work only on the vertical plane i.e. the vibration produces an up and down movement.

The massager simulates the movements carried out in manual massage:

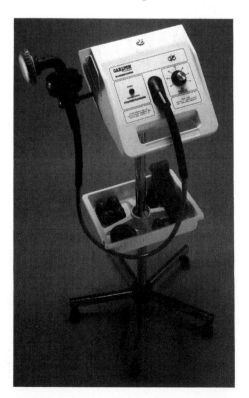

the lighter superficial ones
⟶ effleurage and tapotement
the deeper more penetrative ones
⟶ deep effleurage, kneading, petrissage

This is achieved by using several different applicator heads throughout the treatment.

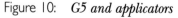

Figure 10: *G5 and applicators*

The manufacturer's instructions should be followed for the correct use of each applicator head.

CARE OF EQUIPMENT

In a busy establishment there are usually several sets of applicator heads to ensure that correct cleansing and sterilisation can take place.

The applicators have direct body contact and the correct hygienic care of them is vital.

Some applicator heads can be washed with hot, soapy water plus antibacterial solution; for example, a sponge applicator. Others require a spirit solution to remove the residue left by the talcum powder which can become ground-in to the applicator.

If an applicator head has been **thoroughly** cleaned and sanitised it should be **absolutely** clean.

The client and mechanical massage

Your client will probably have this treatment:

- to increase muscle stimulation and to have an invigorating massage
- to assist a localised area e.g. for tension, 'spot' reduction.

THE CLIENT SHOULD:

- fully understand the treatment and how it works on the body, particularly the increased heat felt in the skin
- be checked for contra-indications.

Client preparation

Your client will be prepared as for manual body massage (see pages 83–84).

Ideally a short pre-heat treatment would prepare the body to receive maximum benefit from the massage.

The new client should be advised that there is noise from the electrical machine and that it is necessary to move the machine around during the treatment.

• The client feels more comfortable if she/he is aware of what is taking place.

The gyratory massage is usually performed together with manual massage and both machine and hands follow the same massage techniques (see page 88).

The client should be asked regularly if she/he is comfortable, to ensure that the treatment is acceptable and beneficial.

THE THERAPIST USING A GYRATOR MUST:

• check the correct applicator head is used
• not work for too long a time on one area, else bruising can occur
• be advised by the degree of erythema which naturally occurs.

MALE CLIENT/SPORTS MASSAGE/CLIENT WITH CELLULITE

The male client with a developed musculature will probably want to have a longer period of treatment with the gyrator than the client with less developed muscles.

This treatment is ideal for the heavily built male client or the person requiring a deep massage for pre- or post-sport activity.

The client with cellulite will also find this treatment particularly stimulating and beneficial as it can produce a good visual effect on the skin.

Finally, your client will feel relaxed yet invigorated from this massage. The skin will be stimulated as well as the deeper layers of tissue. The skin will normally show a deeper erythema than with manual massage alone.

At this stage it can be soothing for the client to either have:

• a light cologne wiped over the skin
• or a light massage oil effleuraged over the skin.

This can help the client not to feel:

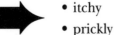

• itchy
• prickly
• dry on the surface skin.

The talcum previously used will, of course, have dispersed by this stage.

Some clients will prefer to shower immediately, or use an

exfoliator sponge to smooth the skin.

The choice is **your client's**. You will have asked about your client's preference before you commenced the treatment. This means that the treatment flows on and finally the client knows what to expect.

Your client will receive the same aftercare as for manual massage treatment (page 84) unless she/he chooses to shower immediately. Then a rest period should follow to allow the body to normalise and recover its own balance.

Contra-indications to mechanical massage

These contra-indications may make it necessary that the client obtains medical approval.

- severe circulatory disorders
- high and low blood pressure
- history of thrombosis
- embolism
- epilepsy
- diabetes
- skin disorders
- any bruising
- recent haemorrhage
- unknown swellings
- warts, moles
- scar tissue
- loss of skin sensitivity
- cuts
- recent operations
- thin skins
- pregnancy
- elderly or emaciated clients
- metal plates/pins/electronic implants

The effects of G5 mechanical massage

it increases the circulation and blood flow to the localised area
supplying nutrients to the skin and muscles

↓

it encourages the elimination of toxins through the lymphatic system

↓

it can penetrate the deeper layers of the skin and assist in the
reduction of fatty tissue

↓

it assists cellulite regions

↓

it is relaxing and can ease tension and muscular aches

↓

it is very invigorating and the entire body is stimulated and energised
after a treatment session

CHAPTER 12 *The sauna cabinet*

This is **dry heat** treatment.

The cabinet is made from pine logs with insulating material to ensure there is no heat loss.

All the internal fitments are also made of pine for safety and hygiene as metal would be unsuitable because it conducts heat.

The cabinet has:

- benches for sitting/lying
- duckboards for standing
- bucket and ladle
- electric stove in a safe position.

The electric stove produces heat. On top of the stove are some coal-like stones.

The stove is thermostatically controlled. This is usually strategically placed outside the cabinet so it cannot be touched by the occupants.

A large **thermometer** should be placed in the sauna.

Water is put on the coals at intervals which produces steam and humidity. This lessens the evaporation of sweat from the body and prevents dehydration.

The manufacturer's instructions stipulate the most suitable temperature for the sauna to be 70°C. This has been calculated according to the body's circulation.

Preparation of the sauna cabinet

- The sauna should be scrubbed with an antibacterial solution *daily* (**clients will often report salons directly to the Environmental Health Officer if they see unhygienic conditions**).
- The wall air vents should be open to allow circulation of air in the sauna.
- The water bucket should be filled (an essential oil may be added for freshness and pleasant aroma).
- A supply of towels should be available for the client's use.
- The sauna should be switched on about one hour before use (or according to manufacturer's instructions).
- The sauna is ready when 70°C temperature has been reached.
- Some clients may prefer a higher temperature. Up to 95°C is usually recommended (check manufacturer's handbook).
- In a large establishment the sauna is left on all day.

AFTERCARE FOR THE SAUNA

- The sauna should be cleaned thoroughly with antibacterial solution.
- The doors should be left open to allow fresh air to circulate.

If a salon is to be cost effective cleaning and sterilising equipment must be considered in the treatment time.

With a partner, set up a time and motion check on how long it takes to clean and prepare a steam bath or sauna.

The sauna treatment

The client should know what to expect.

You will want to advise the client of any **contra-indications** and you will want to explain the effects of the dry heat treatment on the client's body.

The client should be advised to **remove jewellery to avoid heatburn**, and to protect her/his hair. The client should be advised to shower before the sauna.

The general treatment is:

* sauna
* shower/relax – rest period
* sauna.

The client needs to understand the effects on her/his body and the reactions that she/he could expect:

* deep cleansing of the skin
* the quick evaporation of sweat on the skin
* the relaxation of the body created by the sauna/shower and rest time (five to ten minutes alternated with a maximum of twenty minutes)
* the psychological and physical effect of the sauna session.

The client should be given disposable slippers to wear in the sauna (or her/his own rubber shoes or sandals). This is important to prevent cross infection, e.g. verrucas.

The client should be shown the layout of the sauna and it should be explained why the lower benches should be used at first because it is cooler nearer the bottom (heat rises).

The client should be aware that if she/he feels giddy or unwell in any way then there is an **alarm button** to call attention. The therapist should also remind the client that she/he is in the immediate vicinity and is **available for assistance at any time**. Your client can then relax and enjoy the sauna fully assured of the treatment's benefits and of your attention.

SAUNA CABINET

This can hold two or three people if it is small and six or more if it is large.

Clients frequently book sauna sessions on their own in order to have privacy. Some prefer company and bring a friend or two.

This is an ideal time to offer a 'beauty package' and combine treatments for your clients.

CHAPTER 13

Steam treatments

There are a few differences between the steam cabinet and the steam room.

The steam room allows several clients to enjoy a steam treatment together. The main difference is the size of the steam area and that it is totally enclosed. The client's head is not exposed as in steam cabinet.

THIS TYPE OF STEAM TREATMENT IS NOT SUITABLE FOR

- anyone who would find it difficult to have her/his head in a steamy atmosphere, as this can be claustrophic
- anyone who prefers a treatment alone.

Many clients enjoy the opportunity to relax and chat with other people. Clients must be aware of the time (a **clock/timer** should always be in the steam room). The therapist should be available for assistance at all times.

Preparation of the steam cabinet

The single steam cabinet is the most commonly used steam bath. However, in health spas there are also **steam rooms** – also called **steam baths**. These can take large numbers of people seated around the room/bath. They operate differently to the steam cabinet and are usually centrally controlled from a plant room. Hygiene and cleanliness requirements are much the same as the individual cabinet and demand regular checking. This is more difficult as the steam room is in operation all day. *Manufacturer's recommendations must be followed.*

STEAM BATH/CABINET

The steam bath is now usually made of fibreglass for hygiene purposes. Metal cabinets are still available. The fibreglass bath can be easily washed and maintained.

Once the door is open there is:

- an adjustable seat
- a small water tank beneath the seat which is heated by an element.

The tank needs regular filling and checking. There is usually a line indicating where the water level should be. Maintenance of this is vital for hygiene as well as making the bath operational.

The adjustable seat should be attended to for each client to ensure individual comfort.

The therapist must:

- ensure the bath is clean
- check the tank
- put on the steam bath to warm up (temperature should be 50–55°C)
- place suitable towels or paper towels on the seat and on the floor of the cabinet on the stepboard (where the client's feet will rest)
- place a towel over the top of the cabinet to ensure steam doesn't escape while it is warming up.

AFTER USE

- all towels should be removed (paper ones disposed of)
- the cabinet should be thoroughly cleaned with a suitable anti-bacterial cleanser
- the tank level should be checked (when it has cooled)
- the cabinet door should be left open to allow the cabinet to dry.

Preparing the client for a steam bath

Good client preparation ensures that your client can relax and enjoy it.

In your consultation you will have checked for contra-indications and if everything is satisfactory you will proceed. You will, of course, want to explain the effects of the steam bath so that the client understands what changes are taking place on her/his skin and in the body. She/he will also see the importance of showering **before** and **after** the session.

The client should be advised about hair protection and an appropriate covering should be available.

All the client's jewellery should be removed for safety and to reduce the risk of minor burns. Neck chains can become very hot even in moist heat and can burn the skin.

Your client should be allowed to change in private and be given suitable gown or covering to protect her/him.

The steam bath will be ready for use (page 100) but it is always a good idea to make a final check of the seat level while your client is there and to place a fresh towel on the seat just before the client sits down; this demonstrates the standard of hygiene that your salon maintains. Ensure that the client sits comfortably with suitable towel protection around her/his neck and shoulders and explain how easy it is to open the cabinet if she/he wishes to get out. This helps to counteract any fear the client may have of claustrophobia.

The therapist, of course, will be present or in the immediate area all the time. This is a good opportunity to talk with your client about her treatments and the salon's promotions.

Once the 'bath' has maintained its temperature the client can relax for up to 25 minutes. If it is the client's first time ten minutes may be adequate. The **maximum** duration of a steam bath is usually 25 minutes.
After the bath the client should be advised to stand up slowly and then be carefully assisted by you as she/he leaves the steam cabinet or room. Fresh towels or a fresh client gown should be skilfully presented to your client so as to avoid any embarrassment.

The client should then enjoy:

- a **warm** shower
- a relaxation period
- continuing with another treatment, perhaps a body massage.

Your client should feel that the treatment was clean, safe, enjoyable and beneficial.

If your skill, expertise and client handling was appropriate then you would no doubt have a satisfied client.

The effects of steam treatments on the body

increases circulation

↓

which allows the removal of waste products/toxins to be dispersed quickly through the lymphatic system

↓

and fresh nutrients to be stimulated

↓

skin cleansing is deep as sudoriferous glands produce more sweat and sebaceous glands are also more productive

↓

nerve endings are soothed

↓

the warmth assists aches and pains and relaxes the muscles

↓

the metabolism is speeded up

↓

pulse rate increases

Contra-indications

- severe circulatory disorders (high/low blood pressure)
- history of thrombosis/embolism
- respiratory disorders
- epilepsy
- diabetes
- malfunction of the nervous system
- skin disorders
- severe bruising
- recent haemorrhage or unidentified swellings
- warts or moles
- recent operations
- pregnancy
- fever

CONTRA-INDICATIONS WHICH SHOULD BE CONSIDERED BUT WHICH DO NOT NECESSITATE A DOCTOR'S APPROVAL

- immediately after a large meal
- after drinking alcohol
- during a heavy period
- if the client has not eaten for a long period (may feel faint)

CHAPTER 14

The spa pool

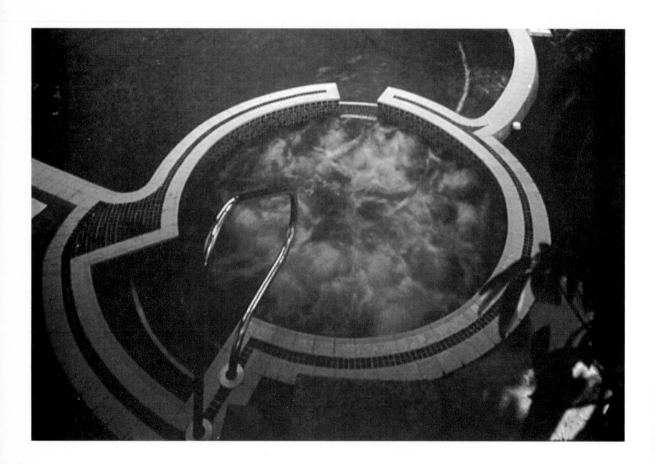

Preparing the client for the spa pool

You will want your client to enjoy this relaxing water treatment. In order to do that she/he must consider certain points and it is your responsibility to advise the client in relation to them.

The client should be aware of any health disorders which would prevent her/him using the spa. If your client is a regular then your detailed client records would indicate if your client was suitable (refer to the contra-indications, page 106).

The client may need to consider hair protection, particularly if the client's hair is permed or coloured.

The importance of skin cleansing before and after using the spa should also be explained to ensure that your client takes every precaution from having a skin reaction to the chemical additives in the water.

In order to gain maximum benefit from the session the client should be advised how to sit comfortably in the spa and to stay in the spa for the time recommended by the manufacturers. This ensures a safe, enjoyable session. The client should also be shown how to use the control panel and the intensity control.

The client should also be advised about the effect of chemicals and water jets on fabric. This can save the company claims for damaged costumes.

Finally the client should be attended. A therapist should be in the area and should be observant. Many accidents have occurred in spas because clients have been unattended and have stayed in the water too long. Refer to the manufacturers' instructions for the maximum length of time allowed.

The client and the spa pool

- Advice should be given regarding contra-indications and suitability for using the spa pool.
- Advice should be given on how to sit in the pool for comfort.
- Advice given on using the operator controls.
- Pre-treatment facilities explained in relation to:
    showering
    hair protection.
- Aftercare should be explained, in relation to:
    shaving
    skin care
    suitability of certain beauty products.
- Use of spa pool should be monitored.
- It is important to observe the spa pool whilst it is in use.

The effects of the spa pool

Your client should be advised of the beneficial effects of the spa pool:

- increased circulation which speeds up the process for the removal of toxins
- stimulation of the skin
- metabolic stimulation
- easy muscular exercise against the jets of water
- a natural relaxation brought about by the pressure jets which stimulate the body's systems.

Contra-indications

These may necessitate a doctor's approval.

- severe circulatory disorders (high/low blood pressure)
- history of thrombosis/embolism
- epilepsy
- diabetes
- spastic conditions
- dysfunction of the nervous system
- skin disorders (allergies)
- severe bruising
- recent haemorrhage/swellings
- warts/moles
- recent operations
- pregnancy
- age of client should be considered (young children, frail person, elderly person)

Maintaining the spa pool

The therapist must be proficient in maintaining the spa pool. Most establishments will have a spa pool which has specific manufacturer's instructions for use. These pools are usually serviced on a regular basis by the manufacturing company.

Sometimes the service is free of charge and only repairs need to be paid for. Alternatively there may be a yearly contract fee.

This means that regular checks are carried out by the therapist or spa staff and only major work is carried out by the service engineer.

Some establishments such as hotels where there is a team of house maintenance people, carry out their own maintenance.

The therapist and/or spa staff are still responsible for checking:

- the hygiene of the pool
- that water filters are functioning properly
- that chemical additives (pH/chlorine) are maintained according to the manufacturers recommendations
- that the temperature is maintained at the correct level
- that the spa area is safe and not wet and slippery
- that record charts are maintained legibly.

The spa usually has its own (power) plant room quite close to it.

The therapist is generally only required to check certain detail in the plant room and to report any malfunctioning.

The filtration system is the key area for concern and therefore needs regular monitoring.

CHAPTER 15 *Sunbed tanning treatment*

Client preparation

- they want a tan
- they want to prepare their skin for a hotter climate
- they want to keep their existing tan
- they want to help with an acne disorder
- they have been advised to use one for medical conditions, such as psoriasis.

When your client comes for a sunbed treatment it is important that during your consultation you have:

- checked for contra-indications or if the client has recently had epilation
- identified your client's skin type
- explained the effects of ultraviolet irradiation on the eyes, skin and skin reactions (see page 112)
- patch-tested the skin (where necessary)
- checked that the client understands the pre-treatment procedures, e.g. showering to ensure that there are no substances on the skin that could cause harmful effects.
- ensure that your client understands the importance of aftercare treatment
- filled in (or begun) a sunbed record card, to ensure that the correct amount of time is spent on the sunbed.

The client should be given the opportunity to see the sunbed before treatment; with the large variety of suntanning machines there are often some that the clients prefer. 'Up and over' sunbeds can be claustrophobic for some clients and can cause stress. It is vital to ascertain this information before the session.

The client should also be advised where the **alarm button** is situated and shown how to use protective eye pads or guards.

During the consultation the client should be advised of the manufacturer's recommended time for each session. This usually corresponds to the salon's course of treatments. However, some clients will prefer less time and some will want more. It is acceptable for the client to have less time but increasing the time is **not** advisable because of over exposure. You will have already explained this to your client.

You will want to ensure that your client enjoys the sunbed session so that means:

- the client's skin is properly prepared
- jewellery is removed
- the client is correctly and comfortably positioned
- eyes are protected throughout the session and the client has been advised of the sensitivity of orifices of the body, e.g. lips, anus
- the client is supervised throughout the treatment
- the 'timer' is set for the appropriate time to ensure a safe treatment
- the client knows that you are there to check on her/him.

REMEMBER

- Always check that **you** are correctly protected from UV rays.

When correct procedures are carried out, clients **do not**

- bang their heads getting up
- slip on the floor
- burn their leg or arm on the edge of the bed which can retain heat
- feel dizzy and sick.

After the session, assist your client and ensure that:

- she/he does not get up quickly
- does not rush to get changed.

Advise her/him of suitable aftercare for skin. Your salon will have products specifically for this purpose and it is vital for the health of your client's skin for it to be treated regularly.

SUNBED TREATMENT CARD

NAME:

ADDRESS:

TEL: (Work)   (Home)

AGE:

DOCTOR:

ARE YOU UNDER MEDICAL SUPERVISION		PRESCRIBED OR TAKING ANY FORM OF DRUG	
DIABETIC	DIURETIC	PREGNANT	TRANQUILISER	ANTIBIOTIC

ARE YOU HYPERSENSITIVE TO SUNLIGHT		DO YOU HAVE A SENSITIVE SKIN

DO YOU SUFFER FROM ANY OF THE FOLLOWING:		ALLERGIES/ASTHMA	BLOOD DISORDER
EPILEPSY	HEART DISORDER	COLD SORES	RENAL DISORDER
SKIN ULCERS	HYPERTENSION	FAINTING	GIDDINESS
VERRUCAS	PRICKLY HEAT	HEADACHES	MIGRAINE
ATHLETES FOOT	VITILIGO	SKIN DISORDERS	ECZEMA
ILL EFFECTS FROM NORMAL SUNBATHING		ABNORMAL BLOOD PRESSURE	

If your client answers in the affirmative to any of the above questions **you should advise** them to consult their doctor **prior to treatment.**

I confirm that to the best of my knowledge I have answered the above questions correctly.
I understand that if the answer is yes to any question I should consult my doctor before using suntanning equipment.
I have read and understood the above and am satisfied that I am suitable for UVA suntanning treatment.

Signature _____   Date _____

SUNBED TREATMENT CARD

NAME:

SKIN TYPE	SENSITIVE		FAIR		MEDIUM		DARK		OLIVE
SUN BED	HIGH PRESSURE		LOW PRESSURE UVA			LOW PRESSURE R-UVA			

Date		No. of Sessions Booked		Length of Session		Amount Paid £
Date		No. of Sessions Booked		Length of Session		Amount Paid £
Date		No. of Sessions Booked		Length of Session		Amount Paid £
Date		No. of Sessions Booked		Length of Session		Amount Paid £

No.	Date	Time	Length	Paid	No.	Date	Time	Length	Paid	No.	Date	Time	Length	Paid
1					13					25				
2					14					26				
3					15					27				
4					16					28				
5					17					29				
6					18					30				
7					19					31				
8					20					32				
9					21					33				
10					22					34				
11					23					35				
12					24					36				

Special advice to the Client on Home Skin Care and Hygiene.

Products purchased for Home Care.

ET1

Figure 11:   *Two-sided sunbed treatment card*

You will offer your client time to relax and adjust, whether or not she/he is having a different treatment next. This is often an ideal time for the client to see any special offers in the salon and gives the opportunity to ask about other treatments.

REMEMBER

- never rush your client after treatment. The body needs time to adjust.

Finally you must ensure that your client's record of sunbed sessions is clearly, accurately and legibly written on a sunbed record card.

Contra-indications

- severe circulatory disorders (high/low blood pressure)
- history of thrombosis/embolism
- respiratory problems
- epilepsy
- diabetes
- malfunction of the nervous system
- skin disorders e.g. vitiligo, chlosma, photosensitivity
- severe bruising
- recent haemorrhage or swellings
- warts or moles
- areas of scar tissue
- areas where there is loss of sensitivity
- cuts/abrasions
- pregnancy
- hormone disturbances (risk of vitiligo and chlosma)
- history of skin cancer or other cancers
- history of herpes
- conjunctivitis
- antibiotics or particular drugs (causing allergy or skin sensitivity)
- fever/illness which need medical attention
- sunburn

Some clients can enjoy the use of sunbeds, others cannot. Explain how you would prepare yourself a 20-point checklist to ensure your client's suitability.

The effects of overexposure

- reddening (erythema) and burning
- histamine is released, the skin itches
- blood vessels dilate
- swelling occurs as fluid builds up in the region causing blisters and pain
- headache occurs and sometimes pain in the eyes
- sickness and diarrhoea can follow.

Prolonged overexposure and this can vary from individual to individual can result in sunstroke.

Sunstroke symptoms are prolonged, sickening headache and sickness/diarrhoea.

- **It is very important that the client's use of the sunbed is monitored closely to avoid overexposure.**

UV radiation treatment considerations

Because of the damage which can be caused by overexposure the client's skin should be:

- free from jewellery
- clean and free from any substances e.g. deodorant, perfume
- the client should have showered before treatment.

The client should have removed any contact lenses.

Eye protection should be worn during use of the sunbed.

UV equipment

Manufacturer's instructions must always be followed when using equipment.

Ultra violet equipment/suntanning beds must be monitored carefully to ensure safe practice.

The procedure for operating a sunbed will be clearly defined in the manufacturer's handbook. The manufacturer's record book ensures that the emission tubes' use is monitored, and that service and maintenance is regularly carried out and that bulbs are replaced. The beds **must** also comply with legislation as specified in the Health and Safety Act, see page 244.

Cleaning instructions are also clearly defined; specific cleansers are recommended according to manufacturer's instructions. It is **vital** that **recommended** cleansers are used because

- they suit the equipment
- they ensure that cross infection does not occur after use

Monitoring of the emission tube's usage has **two** specific functions:

1 the tube usually has a manufacturer's guarantee, so long as the manufacturer's record book is kept accurately.
2 the tube becomes weaker as it ages. This means that the length of sunbed sessions will vary according to the age of the tube, and clients will be made aware of this.

The Law requires that clients:

- are informed by a prominently displayed notice new tubes/lamps have been fitted
- that a prominent notice also warns clients of the effects of UV radiation
- that notices outlining correct procedures are displayed

  this means   **safety** (using eye protection)

  hygiene (ensuring the equipment is clean)

- **adequate ventilation** is vital with sunbeds because of the excess of ozone that the UV rays produce.

---

1 Write to three companies that manufacture sun tanning beds, and obtain details of their equipment.

Compare the product and its cost, running costs and maintenance costs and decide on the one you would purchase.

2 Carry out some research on sensitive skin types and their reaction to ultra-violet rays. Present your findings as an informative chart which could assist therapists in a salon situation.

3 Research sunscreen products and prepare a simple handout leaflet to give your clients a basic understanding of them in relation to the various skin types.

CHAPTER 16   *Infra-red radiant heat radiators*

Client preparation

There are several reasons why a client may have an infra-red treatment:

to aid relaxation
↓
to relieve muscular pain
↓
to relieve pain in the joints
↓
to increase circulation
↓
to heat a substance on the skin

Whatever the reason, it is vital that your client is properly prepared and understands the treatment.

During your consultation you will have checked for contra-indications (see below). It is then necessary to give your client a skin test to ensure she can distinguish between **hot** and **cold**.

This can be carried out by putting hot water in one container and cold water in another and alternating their touch on the client's skin.

Your client wants to enjoy this treatment and in order for it to be beneficial the client **must** be advised to tell you if there is any **discomfort**.

The client should not feel:

→ too hot/burning
→ itchy/prickly
→ sudden head pain
→ faint

YOU WILL WANT TO MAKE THE CLIENT COMFORTABLE

That means:

- the client is correctly positioned in relation to the infra-red radiator with the correct angle for the rays to penetrate
- the infra-red radiator is at the correct temperature to achieve the desired effect
- the client's eyes, head and body areas not being treated are properly protected from the rays (eyes should be covered with wet pads)
- the client is supervised throughout the treatment time
- the 'timer' is set to ensure a safe treatment
- the client knows you are there to check on her/his comfort.

During the session you **must protect yourself** from the radiator. At the end of the session you **must**:

- check your client is comfortable
- ensure that she/he understands the physical effects of the treatment and any homecare advice that you want to give.

NEVER RUSH YOUR CLIENT AFTER TREATMENT

The body needs time to adjust. If you are continuing with other treatment, check that your client is ready to proceed.

THE EFFECTS OF CORRECT INFRA-RED TREATMENT (MILD HEATING)

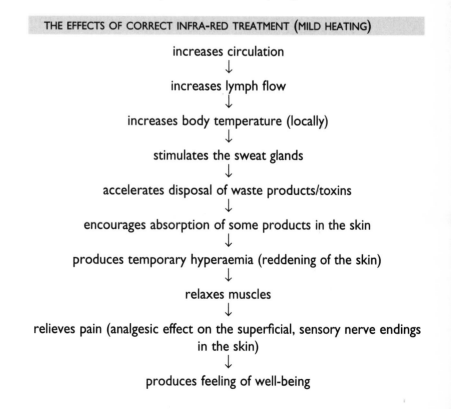

increases circulation
↓
increases lymph flow
↓
increases body temperature (locally)
↓
stimulates the sweat glands
↓
accelerates disposal of waste products/toxins
↓
encourages absorption of some products in the skin
↓
produces temporary hyperaemia (reddening of the skin)
↓
relaxes muscles
↓
relieves pain (analgesic effect on the superficial, sensory nerve endings in the skin)
↓
produces feeling of well-being

- The **infra-red** rays only penetrate the epidermis.

- **Radiant heat** rays are intense and penetrate more deeply into the dermis

THE EFFECTS OF CORRECT RADIANT HEAT TREATMENT (INTENSE HEAT)

produces pain relief by irritating the superficial sensory nerve endings which causes counter irritation.

Your client should be correctly advised of the effects of the treatment and appropriate aftercare of the skin.

1 Design a leaflet for your salon to show your clients the benefits of heat treatments.

2 You are selecting a new infra-red lamp unit for your salon. What do you consider to be the main points for purchasing a lamp?

Detail your considerations.

Treatment considerations

INFRA-RED RADIATION CAN CAUSE:

- injury to the eyes – cataracts
- headaches
- fainting
- burning, due to overexposure, or contact with the appliance.

The client's
- jewellery should be removed
- contact lenses should be removed
- skin should be free from
  - grease/oil
  - ideally the client should have showered and be prepared for treatment as indicated on page 114.

Contra-indications

- diabetes (poor skin sensitivity to heat circulation)
- hypersensitive skin
- loss of skin sensation
- sunburn
- circulatory problems (heart)
- metal pins/plates
- skin disorders
- allergies
- pregnancy

Create three packages to sell to clients and to promote **all** the body treatments that are available in your workplace.

Explain your choice of package.

A LARGE PRODUCT COMPANY TRAINING SCHOOL - INTERVIEW WITH MARIE

When we interviewed Marie, who is the training manager of the UK division of an international product company, the importance of effective client communication was clearly apparent in the business.

Marie trains the company's beauty therapists as tutors to deliver product training to beauty therapists who are given a four-day free training when their establishment purchases the product company's launch package. The latter consists of:

- an electrical machine
- product
- product manual
- posters/samples/bags
- a free four-day product training.

This package costs the establishment an initial £2,400 and training and aftercare sales assistance are always available. The product is only sold through beauty salons so the company sees the importance of a basic product sales training for their customers.

The company structure of the training school division is:

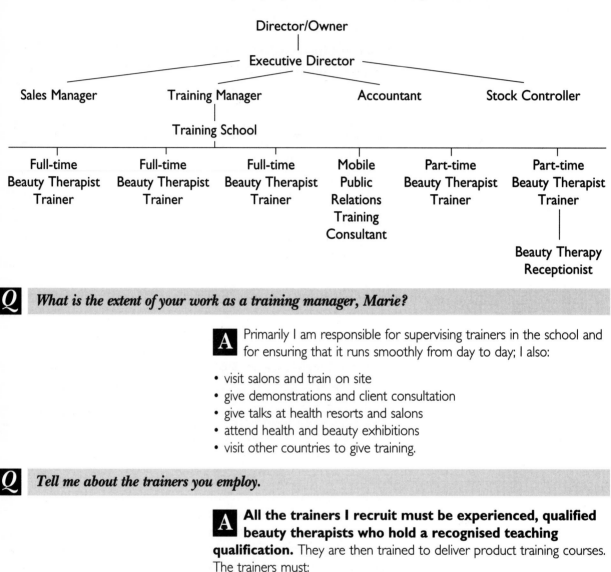

Q *What is the extent of your work as a training manager, Marie?*

A Primarily I am responsible for supervising trainers in the school and for ensuring that it runs smoothly from day to day; I also:

- visit salons and train on site
- give demonstrations and client consultation
- give talks at health resorts and salons
- attend health and beauty exhibitions
- visit other countries to give training.

Q *Tell me about the trainers you employ.*

A **All the trainers I recruit must be experienced, qualified beauty therapists who hold a recognised teaching qualification.** They are then trained to deliver product training courses. The trainers must:

- be over the age of 21 years
- have a mature approach to their work and clients
- demonstrate excellent communication skills
- show care and consideration in their approach to people
- be responsible in outlook and behaviour.

We deliver a four-day intensive training programme, so commitment to work is important. We work as a team. In addition to supervision, I also work with the trainers.

There are three full-time trainers and two part-time trainers who supplement us when we have large numbers on the course.

There is also a travelling beauty therapist, who visits salons and health hydros: her objectives are:

- to improve public relations
- to offer marketing advice
- and to give consultations to individual customers/clients.

Our receptionist deals with a wide range of enquiries, and she is qualified to explain the role of the model in the school. She records important client information to see if the client is suitable to become a model in the training school.

Q **_How does the training school operate?_**

A The school relies on two factors:

- customers to train
- models (clients) for the customer.

The objective of the school is to successfully train up to 20 customers (beauty therapists) each week. To achieve this, the trainers have strict priorities:

- Firstly, the intensive style of the four-day course demands an effective and happy relationship between the trainers and their therapist students.
- Secondly, the trainers have to ensure that the models (filling the role of clients) are happy with their treatments and that the selection of student-model pairings is fair and unlikely to lead to a clash of personalities.

The trainers all have a busy – but hopefully, satisfying – routine; in addition to teaching:

- they have to write up new products
- update the training manual.

As well as all these activities, they have to check that all the routine administration is kept up to date.

Each student has a written record of her progress, rooms have to be prepared for each training session, and the examination papers have to be prepared, the examination invigilated, and the answers carefully marked.

Failures are a great disappointment, and tend to make the trainers feel that they have themselves failed to provide adequate instruction. Thankfully, they are rare.

The customers come to us as a result of the package being sold. As previously stated, we train 20 customers (beauty therapists) each week. This requires 100 models in the course of a week.

Q **_What is the role of the model?_**

A The models (clients) are very important people. They are in an unusual situation in the training school. When people are invited to become models I give them a very detailed explanation of how the school works.

They must understand that:

- we are operating a product training school
- we cannot fit in extra models
- we don't take substitutes
- we must be able to rely on the model
- they need to be punctual
- they need to realise that they are part of the training programme
- they need to be patient and considerate to assist the beauty therapist who is under training.

The models do not pay for the treatments but we do expect them to use our products at home.

The emphasis is on encouraging the person to use the product so that the beauty therapist can see the ongoing results or benefits of using the products.

Many of the models are long-term clients. Some have attended for 25 years, since the company started in the UK, so you see the relationship with our models (clients) is very important.

We, the trainers, complete a detailed record card on the client. This is not left to the beauty therapist, as the models have a different therapist every time they attend.

We know our models well and value their attendance at the school as much as they enjoy coming.

The system works well. It shows a professional situation where treatments and sales complement each other.

Q *Who is responsible in the company for health and safety procedure?*

A I am the trained First Aid officer and I am also responsible for fire evacuation procedure and ensuring that health and safety laws are implemented.

We have regular meetings (monthly if possible) to deal with matters arising in the school and also any changes in procedure.

Q *Finally, Marie, what would you say are the advantages of working as a trainer in a company?*

A The job offers a reasonably good salary, set hours, and rarely requires work at weekends; perhaps most satisfying, one is working as part of a team.

PART 4 *Diet, good health and dietary control*

CHAPTER 17 *New concepts in nutrition*

The working therapist must always be able to answer questions on diet. She/he will understand the importance of regular eating in order to have maximum energy output.

Clients will always want miracles whether it be:

- to lose weight or
- to gain weight.

So where do you start?

National recommendations are always the basis for reliable, tested information and in recent years there has been a great emphasis on nutrition by government and national organisations.

The 1992 Government Report *The Health of the Nation* laid down specific guidelines for diet and nutrition and for a healthy diet.

These are:

- enjoy the food you eat
- eat a variety of different foods
- eat the right amount to be a healthy weight
- eat plenty of foods rich in fibre and starch
- reduce fat intake
- only eat sugary foods occasionally
- look after the vitamins and minerals in your food
- if you drink alcohol, keep within the sensible limits (see Reference Section, page 230).

The theories behind the balance of good health is that no single food contains all the nutrients in the amounts needed to maintain good health, so a variety of foods must be eaten.

This theory also applies to weight reduction.

Dietitians and health professionals generally accept that calorie-restricted diets are not effective. Understanding the **high** calorific value of some foods is important but a **holistic approach** to diet and exercise and **eating the correct balance of food is of major importance**.

The balance of good health

Balance is based on the **five accepted food groups**:
1 Bread, other cereals and potatoes
2 Fruit and vegetables
3 Milk and dairy foods
4 Meat, fish and alternatives
5 Fatty and sugary foods.

Foods in the last group are **not essential** to a healthy diet but add extra choice and are likeable, **but** they must be limited and eaten very sparingly

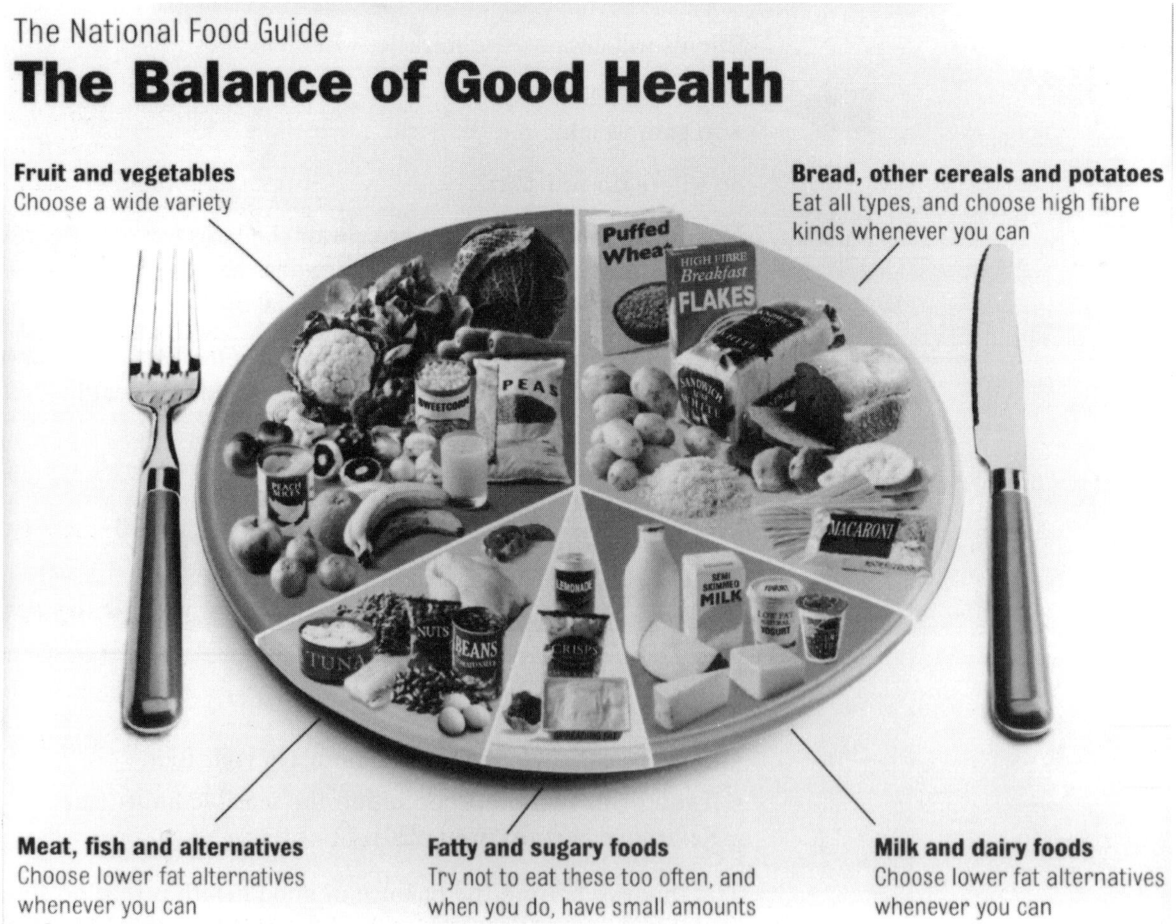
The National Food Guide
The Balance of Good Health
Fruit and vegetables
Choose a wide variety
Bread, other cereals and potatoes
Eat all types, and choose high fibre kinds whenever you can
Puffed Wheat
HIGH FIBRE Breakfast FLAKES
PEAS
MACARONI
LEMONADE
MILK
NUTS
BEANS
TUNA
CRISPS
Meat, fish and alternatives
Choose lower fat alternatives whenever you can
Fatty and sugary foods
Try not to eat these too often, and when you do, have small amounts
Milk and dairy foods
Choose lower fat alternatives whenever you can

Figure 12: *The five main food groups*

Your mid-thirties female client has no idea what healthy eating is all about. She doesn't need to reduce, but she would value your assistance in changing her eating patterns and her food intake.

Detail how you will assist this client.

So what does this mean for the therapist who is assisting her clients with a nutritional programme for:

good health
↓
weight reduction
↓
weight increase?

The therapist will need a good comprehensive knowledge of the latest conception of a balanced, healthy eating plan.

The therapist will then need to be able to assess the client's needs and assist her/him in preparing a healthy eating programme.

Eating for good health

You, the therapist, will have already taken a full consultation and contra-indications to offering dietary advice will be checked (see page 139). You will now want to take more detailed information on your client's food consumption.

—— daily food intake (amount)
—— type of food eaten
—— type of meals consumed (snack pack lunch)
—— fluid consumption
—— occupation (sedentary or active)
—— daily exercise taken
—— sporting activities

When you have this information you will probably ask the client to complete:

• a chart of all food and fluid consumed over an eight-day period.

This will help you to see your client's eating patterns and the type of food she/he enjoys eating and when she/he likes to eat.

If the client wants to eat for good health and not for weight reduction it is a matter of:

• discussing the nutritious content of food
• discussing the way food should be eaten
• establishing a pattern of food intake to ensure maximum energy output after suitable food input.

You will probably want to draw up a schedule of eating for your client and discuss food values.

A simple chart which shows the client's choice of food is one of the best ways to assist the client:

- it gives the client accurate information
- it provides a reference when preparing meals
- it sets out guidelines for nutritious snacks and packed lunches.

REMEMBER

- always keep an accurate record (copy) of any charts that you prepare for your client and make a point of monitoring her situation (examples of food charts can be found on pages 235–7 for your guidance).

A young male client in his early twenties, who lives alone and seldom cooks for himself, is aware that he is not eating a nutritious diet.

His weight is stable but his muscle tone is poor and his complexion pale.

Explain the information you would give him and any other advice or treatments.

CHAPTER 18

Using diet to change weight

The client and weight reduction

In addition to any earlier consultations as already discussed the therapist will need to weight the client and assess how much weight the client needs to lose. A slow weight loss of **one to two pounds a week** is desirable if lean body mass is not to be affected. Slow weight loss allows the gradual metabolism of adipose tissue.

Reference to the **Garrow Weight Chart** is recommended (see Figure 13) and then the therapist must consider the whole person:

- height
- build or figure type
- hereditary factors (see pages 215–216).

The client must feel comfortable with your suggestions about the proposed weight loss and the therapist must ensure that the client sets realistic targets.

SHORT TARGETS ARE BETTER FOR:

- encouraging the client
- keeping to a long term commitment
- seeing effective results.

Once you have the client's commitment to the programme it is important to really **personalise** her eating programme.

The client will need to make a chart of all the food and drink that she/he consumes in a week and how and when she/he eats.

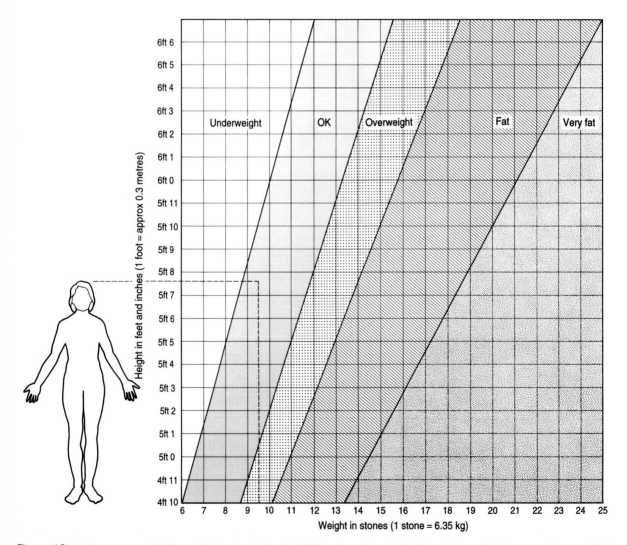

Figure 13: *Are you a suitable weight for your height? This chart is a guide for adults of both sexes. (Source:* Enjoy Healthy Eating *by the Health Education Authority)*

If you have

- established a good rapport with your client
- demonstrated good professional skills and a caring attitude

you will have developed good communication which is vital for dealing with clients, particularly with dietary matters.

It is important to encourage the client to be **honest** especially if the client 'forgets' to record all the food and drink that is consumed.

REMEMBER

- Your ability to assist your client relies on your skills to ascertain correct information and to interpret it so as to give your client the best advice in relation to her weight loss programme.

When you have studied the weekly diet chart you will be able to make recommendations in line with the Healthy Eating Plan.

YOU WILL NEED TO CONSIDER:

- how much food your client needs
- how and when it will be eaten
- what will be eaten.

Refer to the guidelines for preparing a healthy eating programme for weight loss (page 124)

Every client is an individual. Standard charts on food intake can only be guidelines. Clients need to understand:

- the importance of controlled eating (regular food pattern)
- the foods to eat for good nutrition
- the foods to reduce for weight loss.

Your total assessment of your client's dietary needs will culminate in a personal weight control programme.

You will have considered:

- diet
- exercise (refer pages 164–171)
- any salon treatments which could assist the client during her programme.

Your client should leave your premises:

- uplifted and confident in her approach to the programme
- with detailed personalised dietary information to ensure she knows what to eat

- looking forward to hear treatment to assist her weight control programme
- with her next appointment for her weekly weight check.

The therapist's approach in dealing with weight control is a vital link to success. Many female therapists are young, attractive and slim.

Clients can feel embarrassed if they are overweight, talking to someone who does not have a weight problem and they feel that they will not be understood.

This is a **challenge** for the therapist to demonstrate:

- good professional skills with knowledge and expertise
- good life skills with understanding, support and reassurance.

Woman	not overweight	overweight	kilo calories
moderately sedentary	✓		2000
active depending on physical activity	✓		2200–2500
moderately sedentary		✓	1000

Man	not overweight	overweight	kilo calories
moderately sedentary	✓		2250
active depending on physical activity	✓		2700–3600
moderately sedentary		✓	1500

* It is important to note that adolescents' calorie intake is higher and boys require a higher intake than girls. Dietary advice should be taken from a dietitian/doctor regarding adolescents.

Figure 14:   *Sample calorie guidelines, based on the COMA Report (See Reference Section, page 220)*

1 Your client tries all sorts of 'crash diets' but they are not effective over a long period of time.

   Explain how you will proceed.

2 Outline the important factors when assisting a client with a weight reduction programme.

3 You know that clients cheat when they're dieting. Give five points that would really help your clients with this problem.

The client and weight increase

All the detail that has already been discussed is relevant for this client, in addition

- hereditary patterns can play a key part in the underweight client and this can affect any weight increase programme.

HOWEVER, THE CLIENT MUST CONSIDER

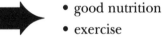

- good nutrition
- exercise

in order to assist the body in its function.

THE CLIENT WILL ALSO NEED TO CONSIDER

- how and why weight is lost.

The cause of this can often be the link to understanding the problem:

- high stress levels
- a quiet worrier

these two conditions can keep the body in a constant state of overworking.

The client needs to be able to discuss all these points with the therapist (see stress chart page 198–9).

A programme for healthy eating and an exercise plan, complemented by relaxing treatments in the salon, can establish a completely new regime for the mind and body.

The client needs to be able to recognise areas that need attention and make a commitment to the programme you will help her/him establish.

Clients that want to increase their weight can afford to eat more of the starchy foods and fat products labelled polyunsaturated.

It is not a good idea for the client to increase foods that are sugary or contain saturated fats because this leads to poor nutrition (refer to chart on page 124).

Weight increase can be more difficult than weight loss in some instances as it often requires a longer period for the body to adjust.

REMEMBER

• good nutrition
• balanced exercise
• relaxing salon treatments
• a personalised, make the most of yourself programme

can create a new physical and mental awareness for this client.

ENSURE THAT YOUR CLIENT LEAVES THE PREMISES WITH ALL THE NECESSARY INFORMATION JUST THE SAME AS YOUR WEIGHT REDUCING CLIENT.

Both conditions are equally important to the individuals.

REMEMBER

• their success depends on your technical and professional expertise
• **their success is your success – satisfied clients return and recommend your services.**

CHAPTER 19 *Other special diets*

The sugar-craving female client

This must be one of the most common client types for the therapist. Often, many therapists will identify themselves in this group at some time.

Initially it is important to establish that the client is not a possible diabetic.

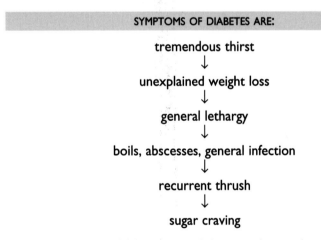

SYMPTOMS OF DIABETES ARE:

tremendous thirst
↓
unexplained weight loss
↓
general lethargy
↓
boils, abscesses, general infection
↓
recurrent thrush
↓
sugar craving

The therapist should be aware of these early warning signs of diabetes.

The sugar-craving female client is affected by her **hormones**. The monthly menstrual cycle means that levels of hormones are continually fluctuating. This varies from one person to another and can cause **PMT** (pre-menstrual tension) and sugar cravings before the menstrual period because blood sugar levels are affected by the hormonal fluctuations.

It requires adjustment to the situation. Eating sugary foods, especially chocolate, can only add to the problem.

- Doctors and dietitians recommend eating high starch food in preference and to avoid missing meals

> Sugar craving is a real problem for many clients.

> Research and consider two different client types and their needs and make constructive plans to assist them.

The importance of regular eating

Many people crave sugar because they skip meals and need an instant lift, so they reach for a sugary snack.

This does nothing to assist the correct process of metabolism and causes a continual rise and fall of sugar levels which can damage health.

- **Regular eating**, three (or more) meals a day, allows the metabolism to work.
- **Skipping meals** or going for long periods without food causes the metabolism to slow down.

To maintain a high energy output the body needs:

- regular nutritious food
- regular exercise.

A POOR DIET CANNOT BE CORRECTED BY VITAMIN SUPPLEMENTS

> Your client is middle-aged and a very poor eater. She asks for your advice during a massage treatment.

> Describe how you could assist her in balancing her nutrients even if she doesn't consume large quantities of food.

The client with water retention

If there is **no** apparent medical reason for the client to have this problem then it may be:

- hormone related
- occupation related (sedentary).

The client with water retention should be

- drinking eight to ten cups of fluid a day (daily recommended amount).

The current view of dietitians is that this can assist the body to achieve a better body fluid balance.

Swimming as an exercise should also be encouraged as it **increases urine production**.

The vegan client on a weight loss/increase programme

This type of client requires specialist advice and dietary information and **must** be referred to a dietitian.

Pregnant clients

Dietary information should **not** be given to pregnant clients.

They must be referred to their doctor or dietitian because they should receive **professional medical advice**.

Supplements and health foods often sold in the salon **should not be sold to pregnant women**.

Recent research has shown that it is no longer necessary for the pregnant woman to eat liver or liver pate. While these foods generally contain a lot of nutrients, the vitamin A content in them is high and in large quantities this vitamin is damaging to the unborn foetus.

The only additional supplement recommended in pregnancy is folic acid but this advice must be given by a doctor.

However, the therapist can play a very **supportive role** with the pregnant client and can assist her to make the most of herself throughout her pregnancy.

Her diet and personal problems can be discussed, especially those physical problems frequently related to pregnancy:

- nausea
- constipation

caused by hormone changes.

The nutritional value of food can also be discussed but any advice relating to the long-term diet or health of the client must be referred to the client's doctor.

Restrictive diets

There are many disadvantages to this type of diet and the therapist should be familiar with them. They:

- are nutritionally unbalanced
- lead to vitamin and nutrient deficiencies
- are anti-social
- do not help to educate the individual in a healthy eating programme.

APPETITE SUPPRESSANTS

These are seldom prescribed by doctors because **they are not effective**, but, they are available from other sources and clients should be discouraged to use them.

HEALTH FOOD MYTHS AND FADS

There will always be a variety of these on the market at anytime.

They

- **can** bring about a quick weight loss.

But

- **can** cause health problems.

THE EFFECTS OF THESE DIETS

They can — cause deficiencies
affect lean body mass
by losing weight too quickly

QUICK WEIGHT LOSS POWDER DIETS

These are usually replacements for normal meals and are very low in calories.

THEY SHOULD ONLY BE USED WITH MEDICAL ADVICE.

DIET FOODS

These are usually a particular number of calories. They consist of vitamin supplements and often have chemical additives.

DIET (BRAN) TABLETS

These are often a very expensive way of buying bran. They are intended to make one feel fuller by increasing the fibre in the system. They can cause 'pockets' of gassiness in the intestines. A large fluid intake is necessary if bran is taken.

> Research three 'quick' methods of weight reduction and explain why they are not satisfactory for a healthy eating plan.

Other diets

High protein diets

consist of milk, cheese, eggs, meat, fish
↓
are high in saturated fat
↓
increase the cholesterol in the blood
↓
are low in fibre
↓
need a high fluid intake

High fat diets

are high in fats and protein
↓
increase the cholesterol level in the blood
↓
restrict the absorption of carbohydrates and fibre

- Any diet which is not balanced according to the Balanced Eating Plan (page 124) will eventually cause deficiencies and contribute to health disorders.

GLUTEN-FREE DIETS

Coeliac disease is a condition where foods containing gluten cannot be digested by the person.

Gluten is a protein found in wheat and other cereals.

Although many people may not have coeliac disease there are individuals who have a mild gluten intolerance so it is advisable for them to avoid:

• biscuits
• bread
• cakes
• wheat flakes
• sausages
• pasta.

Slimming clubs

This is very often a good way of increasing your clientele as well as offering an excellent supportive service.

Clients benefit from:

• a regular weigh-in
• meeting others in the same situation
• sharing ideas
• receiving regular 'pep' talks
• motivation.

The business can also benefit from running a slimming club, especially if a slack time is selected for the event. It often generates new business and gives clients the opportunity to ask questions about weight loss and salon treatments.

The salon slimming club has a distinct advantage over an area slimming club because the weight programme has been personalised.

Your salon decides to set up a weekly weight control club (slimming club) where clients can:

• obtain advice
• be weighed
• receive encouragement.

Explain how you would run the club and make it interesting and inviting to your clientele.

CLIENT COMMENT

I found the therapist I had at the salon was very helpful. She didn't just give me a diet sheet as I had had before. She asked me lots of questions about my eating habits and the foods that I binge on and she showed me how I could use fruit and dried fruit to sustain my sugar problem.

I found this has helped my problems with food and also **helped me** follow a better eating plan.

I would say that the therapist has got to understand your problem. It's no good just telling someone what to eat.

I knew about the 'right' food, I just couldn't stick to it because of my problem with sweets and chocolate.

Weight control reminder

 General tips to help with weight loss:

- eat less fatty foods
- eat less sugary foods
- eat more fibre-enriched foods
- drink plenty of water
- reduce alcohol intake
- eat three regular meals per day to avoid slowing the metabolism.

Contra-indications

- clients aged under 18 or over 70
- anyone receiving medical treatment or following a medically prescribed diet
- anorexia nervosa
- bulimia nervosa
- pregnancy (requires medical dietetic advice)
- food allergies (intolerances)
- vegan (should be referred to a dietitian)
- diabetics (should be referred to a dietitian)
- heart problems

Study one client type for four weeks either for
- weight reduction
- weight control
- weight increase

Design a complete therapist/client programme and monitor the results.

Evaluate your study after the four weeks.

HEALTH SPA – INTERVIEW WITH PETRA, BEAUTY THERAPIST

Petra works in a large health spa in a five star hotel close to Heathrow Airport. The health spa is very impressive with a spectacular glass-enclosed pool atrium, a landscaped waterfall, jacuzzi and a Koi carp pond. Oriental antiques surround the area.

The spa is spaciously laid out with a large reception area, a big well-equipped gym, two beauty treatment rooms, male and female changing rooms, plunge pool, sauna and steam rooms and a relaxation room.

The entire area extends to some 1000 square metres.

Petra has worked at the spa for a year; she is qualified in beauty therapy, reflexology and aromatherapy. Petra completed her studies in England but her home is in Germany. She is employed as a beauty therapist but her work embraces a whole range of health spa duties.

The spa is managed by a supervisor and she is responsible to the hotel duty manager.

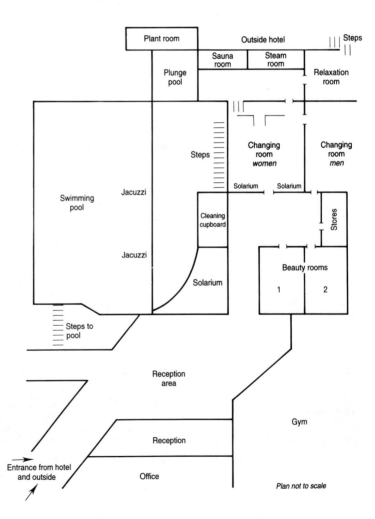

Figure 15:   *Plan of the health spa*

The staff structure is as follows:

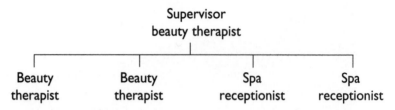

There are three full-time beauty therapists working shifts and two part-time receptionists. These are on the Youth Training Scheme. They have their NVQ level 2 in Leisure and Tourism and they are working in the workplace for their level 2 in Sport and Recreation as spa assistants.

They work from 8.00 am to 1.00 pm and 1.00 pm to 8.00 pm alternate shifts, four days a week.

In addition there are two casual workers who are reception assistants. They work at weekends and other busy times.

The spa provides relaxation and exercise facilities for the hotel guests.

In addition there is a public membership of over 100 people for individual, family or groups. Annual membership can cost £700.

The accounts department processes all the memberships. In the spa only the completed forms and money are taken.

Q *Petra, describe a typical working shift.*

A My working schedule is a five-day week which in effect means six days one week and four days the next. At the moment beauty therapists do not work on Sundays.

Last week my schedule was:

Monday	6.30 am–3.00 pm
Tuesday	11.30 am–8.00 pm
Wednesday	1.45 pm–10.00 pm
Thursday	6.30 am–3.00 pm
Friday	6.30 am–3.00 pm
Saturday	11.30 am–8.00 pm

An early shift starts at 6.30 am. First I get the keys from the hotel duty manager, then I open the health spa and the office.

Next I check the daily message book and the appointment book. I put on the lights and the music system. Then I must go through the spa opening up the facilities. I take the portable telephone with me.

I start with the gym. All the machines have to be turned on. There are 4 bicycles, 2 rowing machines, 2 steppers, 1 treadmill, 6 powercise weight lifting machines and free weights.

Much of the equipment is computerised so that programmes for individual clients can be tailored. We are not expected to prepare programmes ourselves because the machines are personalised and can prepare a programme, including a calorie guide.

Next I prepare the beauty rooms, by turning on the wax heating units and sterilisers. I check the changing rooms and open the doors to the sauna, steam and relaxation rooms. I then go to the plant room. I switch on the sauna and steam. In the winter I turn on the pool lights.

The plunge pool is checked next; the pump has to be inspected to ensure that it is working. Then I test the pool water. Two tests a day are made on all three pools, at 7.00 am and 3.00 pm. The information is logged on Pool Test sheets.

Three separate tests are made:

1 the temperature (not less than 30°C), of the main pool
2 the clarity of the water/chlorine (1.5–2.00) of the main pool
3 pH (7.4 to 7.6), of the main pool

The recommendations are according to manufacturer's instruction. The spa's pools are serviced by hotel maintenance and not by the manufacturers.

The staff are expected to do the testing of the water but if there was a problem with the filters, maintenance would deal with this.

I would add any necessary chemicals to maintain the correct readings. This should be done automatically but it doesn't always reach the level required.

Regular checks ensure safety and cost effectiveness.

7.00   I return to the office in reception and check the daily maintenance checklist (see below). This includes all areas of the spa and everything must be checked to see that it is in working order. If anything is not functional I must contact the cleaner or attend to some things myself such as changing light bulbs.

By this time hotel guests and clients are arriving to use the facilities. They collect their towels which are at reception and if they need to contact us there is an intercom system at reception for them to use.

8.00   Treatments can begin at this time if someone else is on duty, which is usual.

There is a full range of beauty treatments. If I am not giving treatments I am expected to assist people in the gym or clean the beauty rooms as well as work on reception.

Q   *Do you assist clients with all the facilities?*

A   I am not expected to assist guests in the spa, plunge pool or swimming pool. Advice notices are displayed stating contra-indications. There is a monitor at reception for the swimming pool and the jacuzzi as it is impossible to see the pool from reception. There is a telephone situated near the pool for the guests/clients to use if there is a problem.

In the steam room, sauna and solariums there are alarm buttons. These are connected to a display board in reception where a light shows and an alarm sounds.

Clients are advised of pre-treatment facilities (showering) and there are notices advising the client where each facility is situated.

Staff facilities

11.30   Between 11.30 am and 1.30 pm a 30-minute break can be taken. If I want a hot meal I can go into the hotel canteen. Hot drinks are also available there. There is no charge for this. On a late shift the canteen is open from 4.30 pm–6.30 pm so a break must be taken at this time if one wants to take the opportunity of having the hotel food.

I prefer to bring my own food and I don't consume it in the canteen because there is no area for non-smokers.

The rest of the shift carries on with treatments or being at reception.

On a late shift the therapist would have to cash-up at the end of the shift.

3.00   My early shift would finish now. I hand over to the next shift any messages or spa details.

Q   *Do you handle money?*

A   When we take money from clients we have a small cash till. We take the money and then 'post' it on the computer where it goes to the accounts department.

A receipt is issued to the client for cash or cheque but if it's a credit card or a room account a different receipt must be used. These transactions must be 'posted' immediately on to the computer so they can be processed. This is important because guests may be checking out.

Q   *Do you order stock?*

A   I am not generally responsible for ordering stock. The supervisor does this, but because I am the only aromatherapist I am responsible for ordering essential oils.
The system for this is:

1   I have to obtain a purchase request form from the accounts department

2 Then I make the order which must be signed by the accounts department and the hotel general manager

3 I can then place the order by telephone or fax.
I am also responsible for receiving and checking the goods ordered.

Q *Do you cash up at the end of a shift?*

 At the end of the late shift I must:

- check the computer account
- check the money in the till
- balance it
- leave £40 float for the next shift.

I complete daily record sheets for

- the cash
- credit cards
- room accounts.

I put all the cash and receipts in the hotel safe.
At the end of the late shift I repeat the same procedure for opening up the spa, but in reverse.

Q *What benefits do you have working in this situation, Petra?*

 I have a contract of employment which states my conditions. My holidays are 20 days a year and on Bank Holidays I get double time and a day off.
I do not get sick pay and I am not allowed to use the spa facilities. Only management is allowed to do so.

Q *Are you offered a subsidised membership?*

 No. My wages are paid every two weeks and I am paid hourly. I started at £3.50 an hour but now receive £4.25 per hour.
There is no commission and no opportunity to increase my earnings. I understand that there is an opportunity to receive a company bonus. I haven't received one yet. This would be good.

Q *Do you wear a uniform?*

A Uniform is provided: green tracksuit bottoms and a white tee-shirt or polo neck.

Q *Do you have any opportunity for further training?*

A No, initially I was shown the spa routine by the supervisor. I have had beauty product training when we changed our products.

We are trained (twice a year) in fire evacuation procedures. This includes:

- which fire extinguisher to use
- where to go in the event of a fire alarm.

We are responsible for getting the clients/guests to safety.

We are advised of health and safety procedure but there are notices in the office.

There is no one trained in First Aid in the spa but there are first-aiders in the hotel.

Q *What about handling complaints? Is this one of your responsibilities?*

A Naturally, I am expected to deal with complaints but if it is out of my control I can refer it to the supervisor. After that it must go to the duty manager. For example, the pool area is often used for major dining functions. This means it is closed and clients can become difficult about this. If I have tried to deal with the matter this would then be referred to the duty manager.

Q *Do you enjoy working in this environment?*

A Yes, it is a pleasant atmosphere and I enjoy the work and the clientele.

PART 5 *Exercise*

CHAPTER 20

Clients and their need to exercise

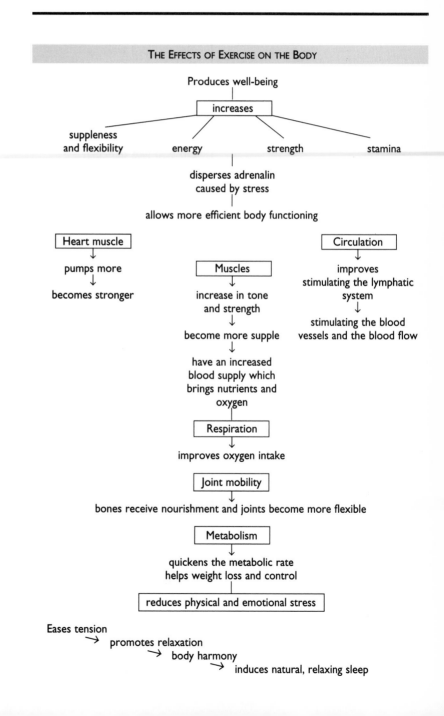

THE EFFECTS OF EXERCISE ON THE BODY

Produces well-being

increases

suppleness and flexibility · energy · strength · stamina

disperses adrenalin caused by stress

allows more efficient body functioning

Heart muscle
↓
pumps more
↓
becomes stronger

Muscles
↓
increase in tone and strength
↓
become more supple
↓
have an increased blood supply which brings nutrients and oxygen

Circulation
↓
improves stimulating the lymphatic system
↓
stimulating the blood vessels and the blood flow

Respiration
↓
improves oxygen intake

Joint mobility
↓
bones receive nourishment and joints become more flexible

Metabolism
↓
quickens the metabolic rate
helps weight loss and control

reduces physical and emotional stress

Eases tension
→ promotes relaxation
→ body harmony
→ induces natural, relaxing sleep

When clients want to develop an exercise routine it is important to find out what sort of exercise they would enjoy and what exercises their muscles need.

A few simple questions designed as a questionnaire could save a lot of time in planning and calculating your clients needs.

A questionnaire could look like this:

	Yes	No	Sometimes
Do you enjoy exercising alone?			
Do you enjoy vigorous exercise?			
Do you like walking?			
Do you like swimming?			
Do you like tennis?			
Do you like jogging?			
Do you like competitive sports?			
Do you like aerobics?			
Do you like dancing?			
Do you like cycling?			

Figure 16.1:   *Sample exercise questionnaire*

If you can include a wide range of sports or exercise activities it will help you to gain a picture of your client's view towards exercise.

What are your client's needs?

A self-assessment sheet can assist you in assessing your client's needs and will help her/him to recognise their own particular needs.

	Yes	No	Sometimes
Do you find it difficult to bend and put on tights or socks? (SP)			
Do you get out of breath easily when walking uphill . . . on flat ground? (S)			
Does your back ache after climbing stairs? (BS)			
Do your legs ache after climbing stairs? (LS)			
Do you get cramp after climbing stairs or walking? (LS)			
Do you find your neck and shoulders feel stiff after simple shoulder exertion? (F)			

Figure 16.2:   *Exercise self-assessment sheet*

- If you then tell the client the explanation of your questions she/he will understand her/his personal exercise needs.

BS	=	back strength
SP	=	need to be more supple
S	=	need to build up stamina
LS	=	leg strength
F	=	more flexible joints

A simple test to assist in assessing body fitness

This is based on the Kasch Boyer Step Test.
1 You will need a step box or bench 30 centimetres high. Your client must step up on to the step bench with both feet then step down again at a pace of once every two seconds, for three minutes.
2 After three minutes – stop. Wait five seconds and then test your wrist pulse over the next 60 seconds

Pulse rate: less than 85 – very fit
over 85 but
less than 97 – fit
over 105 – you need to get fitter

If you are male subtract five beats per minute from these figures.

If you are over 40 years old add two beats per minute. For each ten years over forty add two beats.

Client types

THE UNFIT CLIENT

If the client is very unfit it is important to explain:

- the need to exercise all the muscle groups in the body without overworking any one group.

If your communications with your client have been effective your client will have developed a good rapport with you and will trust your technical skills and understanding.

It is vital now to ensure that she/he understands every aspect of what she/he has to do.

CHAPTER 21

The exercise plan

KEY FACTORS ARE:

- good preparation of client – especially warming up before exercise
- give clear instructions → an explanation
                          → a demonstration
- client and therapist participation
- correct finishing techniques.

GOOD PREPARATION

After checking for contra-indications in your consultation your client should be advised to stop exercising if she/he feels:

- any pain (especially in the chest)
- dizziness
- feels sick

  or movements become uncoordinated.

BREATHING

It is also important to ensure your client understands the importance of correct breathing not in the technical sense but in a basic way. The client should understand:

- the need to provide oxygen for the muscles during increased activity.

BEING READY FOR EXERCISE

Your client must be advised that:

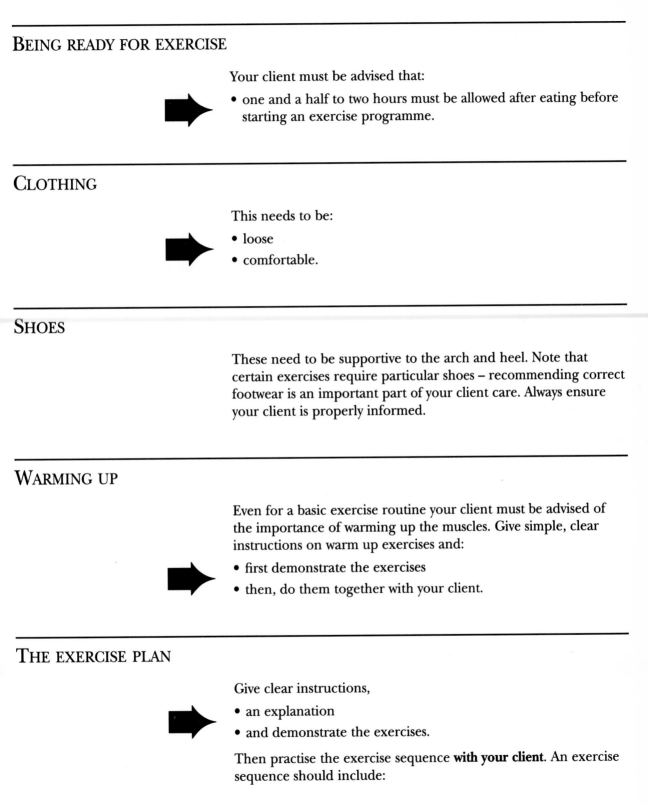

- one and a half to two hours must be allowed after eating before starting an exercise programme.

CLOTHING

This needs to be:

- loose
- comfortable.

SHOES

These need to be supportive to the arch and heel. Note that certain exercises require particular shoes – recommending correct footwear is an important part of your client care. Always ensure your client is properly informed.

WARMING UP

Even for a basic exercise routine your client must be advised of the importance of warming up the muscles. Give simple, clear instructions on warm up exercises and:

- first demonstrate the exercises
- then, do them together with your client.

THE EXERCISE PLAN

Give clear instructions,

- an explanation
- and demonstrate the exercises.

Then practise the exercise sequence **with your client**. An exercise sequence should include:

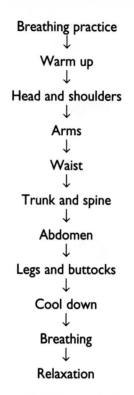

Breathing practice
↓
Warm up
↓
Head and shoulders
↓
Arms
↓
Waist
↓
Trunk and spine
↓
Abdomen
↓
Legs and buttocks
↓
Cool down
↓
Breathing
↓
Relaxation

The importance of **correct finishing techniques** cannot be emphasised too much.

The major point with client care and exercise is to encourage the client to enjoy:

- the exercise routine
- the benefits of the exercise.

Good breathing and relaxation at the end of the routine will ensure that the body **normalises** and reaches its own **equilibrium**, while the effects of the activity continue to benefit the client producing **well-being** and increased mobility.

Your client says she/he never bothers with warm up and cool down when exercising because 'it's a waste of time'. She/he frequently has a headache after exercise. What is your advice?

The unfit client will soon become fitter if the therapist can ensure that the client maintains enjoyment of the activity.

Once clients have gained suppleness and joint flexibility they will be ready to progress to the next stage.

SOME BASIC EXERCISES

The following exercises are basic strengthening exercises and should each be repeated five to ten times depending upon the fitness of the participant. The repetitions can be increased with practice. For further information on exercise techniques, and for more detailed exercise routines, refer to: Rosser, M. (1995) *Body Fitness and Exercise – Basic Theory and Practice for Therapists*, London: Hodder and Stoughton.

Exercises to strengthen leg muscles

1 Stand with the feet apart and the legs relaxed so that the knees are slightly bent. The pelvis should be tucked under and the back kept straight. Bend and straighten the legs keeping the heels on the floor.

Note: Avoid deep knee bends as these put too much pressure on the knees. Make sure that the angle between the calf and the upper leg is always more than 90°. Concentrate on controlled rhythmic breathing and smooth movements. A chair may be used for support.

Or
Stand with one foot forward the other one back (holding onto a chair or wall for support if necessary). Bend both knees so that the back one moves towards the floor, then straighten the legs.

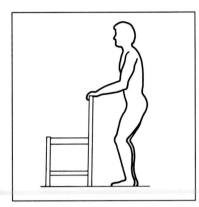

Exercise 1a

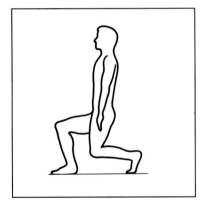

Exercise 1b

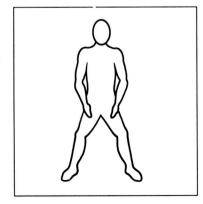

Exercise 2

2 Stand with the feet more than hip distance apart and bend and straighten the legs. Keep the back straight.

Exercise 3

3 Standing with the feet only slightly apart and the arms out to the sides (below shoulder height), jump the feet wide apart and back together again. Make sure that the knees are bent and above the ankle upon landing and that the heels make contact with the floor. This exercise should only be performed by people who are fit.

Exercises to strengthen the abdominal muscles

((for the straight abdominal muscles):

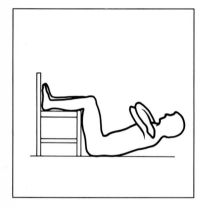

Exercise 4

4 Curl-ups: lie on the back with the legs bent and the feet flat on the floor. Make sure that the lower back is kept flat on the floor throughout these exercises. To help keep the lower back flat, the lower legs may be placed on a chair or bench. Keep the movements smooth and breathe out on curling up, in while lowering down. It is important not to drop the chin to the chest – imagine that an orange is held under the chin at all stages of the exercise.
    Note: Curl-ups differ in intensity depending on the position of the arms:
    Easy • arms by the sides of the body
    ↓   • hands on the thighs sliding up towards the knees and back
          • opposite hands on shoulders, arms bent across chest
    Hard • hands on the ears, elbows out

Exercise 5

5 Reverse curls: lying on the back, lift the legs and curl the hips off the floor. Do not let the legs swing over the head. Keep the whole exercise controlled and smooth.

Exercise 6

(for the oblique abdominal muscles):
6 As for curl-ups but, using alternate arms, reach for the outside of the opposite knee.

Exercise to strengthen the back

Exercise 7

7 Lie down facing the floor. Slowly raise the head and shoulders off the floor, and lower. Do not continue the lift further than a point of comfort. Control breathing – out while lifting and in while lowering. Keep the head in alignment.

Exercises to strengthen the chest muscles and the back of the upper arms

8 Push-ups: these are done by placing the hands a little more than shoulder width apart and straightening the arms to push the chest away from the hands. They can be performed standing with the hands on a wall and the feet a distance from the wall which is comfortable for the participant, or with the hands on the floor and the body in a kneeling position. Control the breathing – in while pushing away.

Exercise 8a

Exercise 8b

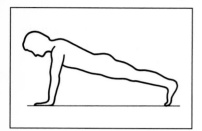

Exercise 9

9 Full push-ups, where the whole straight body is pushed away from the floor and the weight taken on the toes, should only be performed by those who are fit.

1 Your client is not coping with a simple exercise plan and feeling very fed-up and disappointed with her/his own poor attitude. The client admits that she/he really only enjoys body massage.

How would you proceed?

2 Elderly people have specific needs for exercise. Explain these in relation to a simple exercise programme.

EXERCISE AFTER ILLNESS

This needs to be **slow and gentle** and take place in very **short sessions** rather than long ones.

Clients need to know that **you** understand the problem and that there is no emphasis or pressure on them.

The body must rehabilitate itself, slowly increasing energy flow and combating muscular fatigue.

Light exercise – simple sequence and suitable rest/relaxation – is necessary to meet recovering clients' needs.

CHAPTER 22 *Psychological benefits of exercise*

Many clients will seldom think about the psychological benefits of exercise.

> They need to realise that exercise is not just associated with **physical fitness** but with **mental alertness** and **relaxation** as well. There is an **exercise for everyone**. The therapist can assist her client in finding the most suitable one.

If you are giving a stressful client massage, aromatherapy and other stress-relieving treatments, it is helpful to suggest the value of exercise to help them in their daily life.

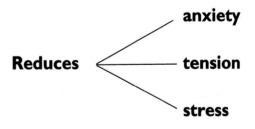

Reduces → anxiety
Reduces ← tension
Reduces → stress

All people respond well to exercise. Clients need to be reminded of the **value of their own body processes in bringing about internal harmony.**

Salon treatments and salon home exercise plans can assist the achievement and maintenance of psychological harmony.

CHAPTER 23

Types of exercise

Isotonic exercise

ISOTONIC = ACTIVE EXERCISES

produces movement in muscles and joints causing lengthening and
shortening of the muscles
↓
develops muscle strength and flexibility
↓
improves respiration
↓
increases circulation
↓
utilises energy

Isometric exercise

ISOMETRIC = RESISTIVE EXERCISE

contracts the muscles without movement
in the joint
↓
increases muscle tone without increasing
muscle length
↓
muscles contract against a resistance
↓
improves muscle strength
↓
allows anyone to exercise who may have a problem with active
exercise

Aerobic exercise

> Aerobic = exercise which uses the entire system of carrying oxygen
> through the body to the muscles

tones muscles
↓
strengthens ligaments and joints
↓
strengthens the heart and lungs
↓
consists of a choice of different types of exercises
that put constant demand on the cardiovascular
system, raising the pulse rate up to
150 beats a minute
↓
includes swimming, jogging, aerobics classes
↓
increases energy and fitness

Consider the type of exercises that three different client types may need.

Design three separate charts that you could show clients before you demonstrate, and a step by step leaflet guide for them to take away with them.

Consider age, suitability, safety, benefits, enjoyment.

CLIENT'S COMMENT ON THE THERAPIST'S HELP WITH EXERCISE

Difficult really – there was I 'wanting' to exercise but knowing deep down I didn't, probably because I was overweight.

The therapist didn't really say too much about exercise; she talked about diet and salon treatments and finally I decided to have a course of aromatherapy and G5 (mechanical massage) treatments.

I started to watch my diet – well, a little. I can't be good for long, but I did feel better in myself and lighter. I didn't lose much weight but I looked better in my clothes.

After about five treatments the therapist suggested swimming. I felt better and looked better so I went and really that's just right for me. I like slowly moving through the water and I don't feel like I'm exercising.

I think the therapist was very quick to assess me. She really knew my personality and everything developed gradually.

She has helped me become a regular swimmer and a fitter person.

Different exercise methods

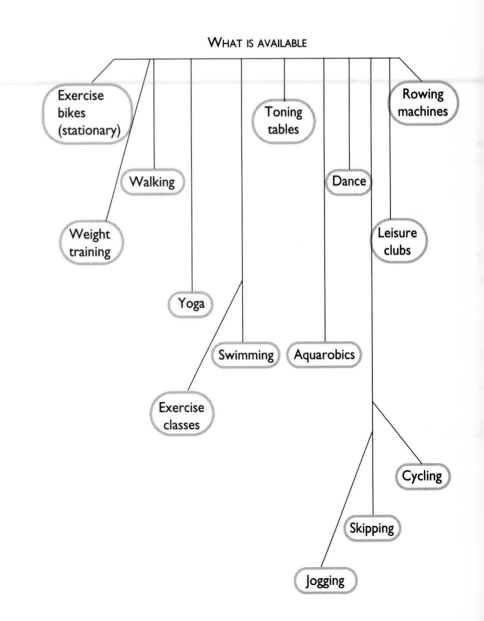

WHAT IS AVAILABLE

Exercise bikes (stationary)

Walking

Weight training

Yoga

Swimming

Exercise classes

Toning tables

Dance

Aquarobics

Rowing machines

Leisure clubs

Cycling

Skipping

Jogging

Walking

good for mobility and relieves stress
and tension
↓
improves circulation
↓
it is a gentle exercise suitable for older
or recovering people

BRISK WALKING

builds stamina
↓
so: works the heart and lungs,
↓
tones muscles
of the feet, legs, abdomen, buttocks,
back, arms and shoulders
↓
strengthens bone ligaments and joints
↓
increases energy levels
↓
costs nothing
↓
good for socialising
can be done alone,
with friends or in a club

Jogging

requires a good warm up
↓
good for stamina, tones and strengthens muscles,
especially the gluteals and the legs
↓
increases energy level
↓
works the heart and lungs
↓
good running shoes are needed
↓
a soft running surface (grass) can be
more gentle on the joints
↓
requires a progressive cool-down period
↓
costs nothing (except the cost of the shoes)
↓
good for socialising: can be done alone, with friends
or there are clubs to join

Jogging is not good for anyone with arthritic hips or legs or anyone who is very overweight.

Skipping

good for the total figure
↓
tones arm, leg, thigh and buttock muscles
↓
tones the pectorals
↓
strengthens the back
↓
increases energy levels
↓
works the heart and lungs
↓
skipping can be done to music
↓
requires good supportive shoes to prevent any shocks to the joints
↓
low cost (cost of shoes and skipping rope)
↓
can be enjoyed alone, with friends or in groups

Swimming

excellent for strength, stamina
and suppleness
↓
does not strain any part of the body as
the body is supported by water
↓
increases energy levels
↓
increases the circulation and stimulates
the respiratory system
↓
all muscle groups are exercised
↓
suits everyone, especially the arthritic, the back-pain
sufferer and the overweight person
↓
a good aerobic exercise when done
quickly and constantly
↓
low cost
↓
can be done alone, with friends,
at leisure clubs

Cycling

requires a good warm-up
↓
excellent for stamina and strengthens the
muscles of the back and legs
↓
increases energy levels
↓
increases the circulation and
stimulates the respiratory system
↓
low cost (once a bicycle is bought.
One can also be borrowed or hired)
↓
can be done alone, with friends
or there are clubs

Exercise classes

These can include

Aerobics   Circuit   Keep-fit
training   to music

provide a total workout
↓
good for stamina, strength
and suppleness
↓
increase energy levels
↓
increase circulation and stimulate
the respiratory system
↓
moderate costs
↓
are a group exercise or can be done
alone, using exercise videos

    KEY POINT

• **The exercise class must suit the individual's level of fitness.**
Good preparation, warm-up and cool-down are vital.

Dance

good for strength, stamina, suppleness
and mobility especially feet, lugs, buttocks
and back muscles
↓
requires a good warm-up
↓
special supportive shoes required
↓
increases energy levels
↓
increases the circulation
↓
moderate cost for group classes
↓
good for socialising with friends

Yoga

a sequence of positions that improves
the condition of the body
↓
good for suppleness
↓
gentle and controlled movement
↓
strengthens muscles in the abdomen,
hips, back and thighs
↓
helps breathing and relaxation
↓
reduces stress and muscular tension
↓
promotes well-being
↓
improves posture and balance
↓
low cost (depending on the class)
↓
can be done alone or in groups

You have been asked to make an exercise video for open day at your establishment.

a) Consider the types of exercise you would include.

b) How you could really make this a key feature in the open day?

c) Finally, produce your video with the help of some of your colleagues.

Leisure or fitness clubs

Membership can be expensive but there are many benefits. These provide:

• a variety of equipment
• swimming pool
• spa
• steam and sauna baths
• multigyms
• a good environment for socialising.

A MULTIGYM

The client will be offered a personalised exercise programme following a fitness assessment.

The use of the multigym is designed to be progressive. The client follows a routine which leads from one piece of equipment to the next; exercising different muscle groups and developing personal fitness.

Each piece of equipment has controlled adjustments and resistance levels.

The multigym offers a complete training programme and when used regularly and under correct supervision it can offer excellent benefits.

EXERCISES

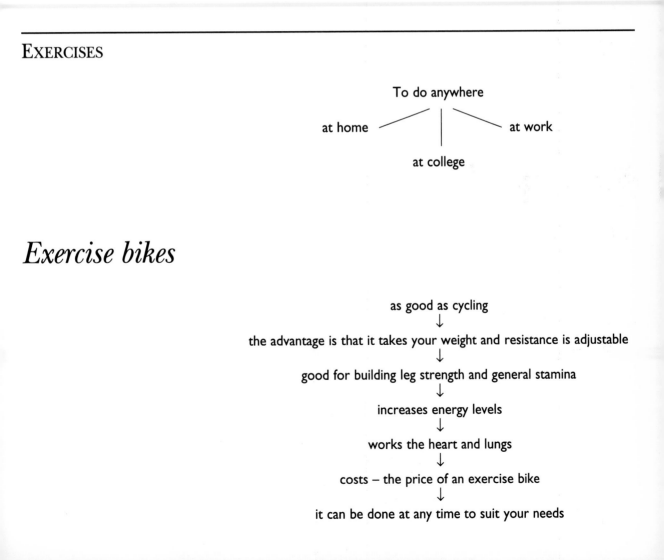

To do anywhere

at home

at work

at college

Exercise bikes

as good as cycling

↓

the advantage is that it takes your weight and resistance is adjustable

↓

good for building leg strength and general stamina

↓

increases energy levels

↓

works the heart and lungs

↓

costs – the price of an exercise bike

↓

it can be done at any time to suit your needs

Muscle-toning tables/machines

various types which can perform one exercise
routine or several sets of exercise patterns
↓

exercises are isometric so they increase
flexibility and tone the body without
straining joints
↓

suitable for most people at any level
of fitness
↓

the table supports the body so fatigue
should not occur
↓

courses of muscle toning can be
expensive in salons and leisure clubs
↓

individual cost of table
very expensive
↓

good for socialising, going as a group or for
anyone who 'doesn't like' the idea of too much exercise

Rowing machines

good for building
strength and stamina
↓

exercise muscles of the back, leg,
arm, abdomen, buttocks
↓

increase circulation and
energy levels
↓

once in place the machine can be
used at anytime to suit you
↓

Avoid if you have any back or
shoulder problems
↓

can be costly – cost of
the machine is quite high

Aquarobics

Aerobic exercise in water.

a stimulating workout with
low strain on joints
↓
tones and strengthens muscles
↓
increases flexibility and
suppleness
↓
good exercise for the heart
and lungs
↓
suits many types of people

young   disabled

mature   arthritic/rheumatic
sufferers

pregnant women
↓
can be done alone or with a group
at a swimming pool
↓
low cost

Weight training

increases strength and stamina
↓
increases suppleness
↓
a variety of weight training programmes include
light weights and heavy weights
↓
good supportive, strong shoes are needed
↓
at first professional instruction is advisable for safe
training and correct lifting method
↓
classes can be for individuals or groups
at leisure centres or clubs
↓
inexpensive if you buy weights for home use.
Otherwise the cost of weights or cost of belonging to a
club or class where the use of the weights are included, can vary

1 Your overweight mid-twenties female client has a clear expectation of who she wants to look like, so much so, she presents you with a picture of a trendy supermodel.

Describe how you will consider your client's **entire** body programme in relation to her needs.

2 A young female client (18 years old) has recently recovered from glandular fever and has been medically advised to consider an exercise programme.

Design an exercise plan for her including home exercises.

INTERVIEW WITH NICKY, LEISURE CLUB SUPERVISOR AT BURNHAM BEECHES HOTEL IN BUCKINGHAMSHIRE

Nicky works in a leisure club in the hotel. She completed her studies in Leisure and Recreation at college five years ago. After a two-year training period she worked as a leisure club attendant in an hotel complex.

She is currently leisure club supervisor. The leisure club is situated within the hotel which is an elegant 18th-century Georgian house.

The interesting aspect of Nicky's work is that she decided to train in beauty therapy while working as a leisure club attendant. Her interest widened into the health and beauty field and Nicky has recently qualified in beauty therapy and aromatherapy at a local college, through the ITEC examination system. She intends studying reflexology next year.

Now in her capacity as leisure club supervisor, Nicky is keen to develop a beauty business in the leisure club.

 Tell me about the leisure club, Nicky.

 The leisure club is small but friendly. It has about 170 members and the age range tends to be young families and more senior couples. I think that the club appeals to the more mature age range because it is small and quiet.

The club is, of course, also used by guests visiting the hotel, but it is never busy; it always retains its quiet atmosphere.

 Who is on the staff?

 I am the only full-time member of staff and my job title is leisure assistant/supervisor. I have more responsibilities than the other staff.

The staffing structure is:
The supervisor (one)
I work full time Monday – Friday, 9.00 am–4.00 pm.
There are four casual staff
They work the remaining hours.
The club is open Monday – Thursday, 7.00 am–9.00 pm,
Friday and Saturday, 8.00 am–10.00 pm, Sunday, 8.00 am–9.00 pm
I am responsible to the duty manager.
I assist and advise the casual staff.

Leisure club structure
Hotel
General manager
|
Duty manager
|
Leisure supervisor
|

| Casual spa assistant | Casual spa assistant | Casual spa assistant | Casual spa assistant |

 Q *Do you receive on-going training in the Leisure Club?*

 A Certainly in First Aid. We are currently developing a full training programme.

Q *Are you expected to train the casual staff?*

A Yes, I teach them all they need to know to do the job.
We do not have to handle any money transactions. This is dealt with by the general manager and main reception. We give out information only.

Q *Do you have a contract of employment?*

A Yes.

 Q *What benefits do you enjoy?*

 A I have four weeks holiday a year. I do not work weekends but if I work Bank Holidays I receive double time and get a day's holiday.
I am paid if I am off sick.
I have free lunches – a hot meal or sandwiches.
I am able to use the facilities anytime I am not working.

I can also use other group hotel facilities and I receive a reduction on my hotel booking at other hotels in the group.

Casual staff have similar benefits to me: but they cannot use the Club's facilities and receive double pay for Bank Holidays.

  What do your duties include?

 My duties are:

   • the cleaning and maintenance of the spa and pool
• the ordering of chemicals and other cleaning materials (the duty manager usually does this)
• designing individual fitness programmes
• organising the shift rota
• budget control.

There is always a lot of cleaning to do.

Daily cleaning includes:

• scrubbing mats
• mopping floors
• sweeping floors
• polishing (surfaces)
• scrubbing showers
• changing shower curtains
• cleaning gym equipment
• cleaning the sunbed and the room
• cleaning the toilets and sinks.

Weekly cleaning includes:

• cleaning lockers
• scrubbing pool area
• checking gym equipment.

I do clean the gym and I carry out a **weekly maintenance check on:**

• the exercise bike
• the rower
• the multibench
• sit-up bench
• free weights.

  Do you serve refreshments for clients?

 No, these are available from the bar if they want to order them. However, we are going to have vending machines installed in the club quite soon.

Cleaning is obviously a major part of your work, does this become a strain?

A Not really, you get used to the pattern of work and then it is all in a day's routine. Cleaning and maintenance form the day's work, for example the maintenance of the spa and pool. Everyday readings are taken at four-hourly intervals when the chemical levels and the temperature are checked.

The pool is maintained around 29°–30°C. The spa's temperature is maintained at 40°C or just below.

Once a week the pool receives a full maintenance check. That means:

- the scum line and surrounding edges in the pool are cleaned
- the clarifiers (in the filters) in the pool are changed – these keep the pool clean
- the pool is backwashed to maintain a clear appearance
- the bottom of the pool is hoovered
- the pool brominator is checked for level of bromine (the brominator is like a barrel which contains bromine (chemical) tablets). This is automatically diffused into the pool through control boxes.

Similarly, the spa is maintained once a week, as follows:

- the water is emptied and refilled
- the brominator is checked for level of bromine
- barrels of pH^+ chemical and pH^- chemical are checked to see the correct level is maintained.

The club functions well with regular maintenance, but if there are any major problems e.g. the filters break down, this is dealt with by the maintenance company who supplied all the equipment. They offer a 24-hour service, but due to demand this does mean that we could have to wait the whole 24 hours.

 Do you have a lot of client contact?

A Yes, because the club is relatively quiet I get to know the clients really well.

They ask for advice on the gym and personal advice for healthcare. They like you to be knowledgeable and friendly.

Client communication is seen to be very important and a personal service is vital.

Do you enjoy your working environment?

A Yes, the hotel is happy with the club being small and relatively quiet and personal and it's a pleasant place to work.

The management are keen for me to develop beauty therapy treatments as an extension of the services offered.

I became interested in beauty therapy whilst working in leisure which was why I decided to train. Now I'm looking forward to using my skills in this hotel and to extend the services of the leisure club. Time management and planning will be my next priority.

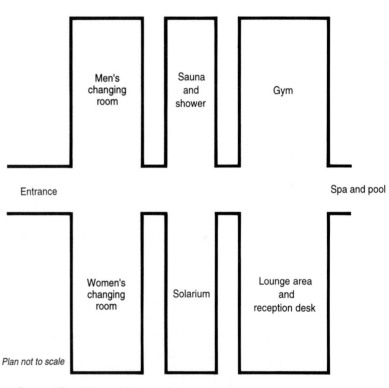

Figure 17:   *Plan of leisure club*

PART 6 *Life skills*

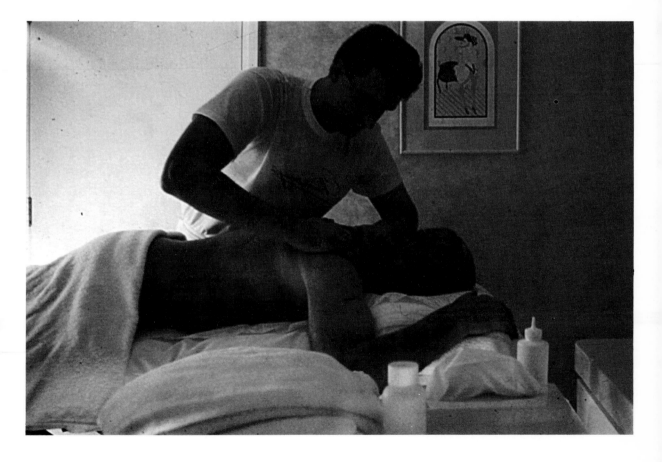

CHAPTER 25 *The therapist's need for a variety of life skills*

Your clientele expect a lot from you and the services your salon offers.

Clients having beauty treatments want to talk about beauty, health, health problems, exercise and diet and a large variety of topics related to these subjects.

They expect **you** the therapist to **know** about the topics and to be able to offer **useful** information regarding their comments.

In relation to health problems it is always advantageous to know about disorders and illnesses. Your basic training includes a variety of these in relation to the body's systems and its disorders. Knowing the name and description of a disorder or illness is not enough when your client wants to discuss various aspects of the problem. So ongoing reading and learning is vital for the therapist.

Your knowledge can be extremely useful in identifying some of your client's problems.

Just as you must be able to identify and know the difference between eczema and athlete's foot, so is it very useful if you are able to identify various stress-related symptoms in your client which may well show themselves in a physical way, e.g. skin blemishes or a tight, tense face and body.

You are aware of **the need** to give your client the best treatment.

This means that **you must be able to offer your client comfort and security and professional skill during the treatment.**

Comfort and security means that the clients find themselves in a friendly caring environment where the therapist demonstrates life skills as part of the treatment.

Life skills incorporate a range of skills including the vital 'listening skills'. Clients' needs vary and some clients **only** require a good listener, whilst others want as much communication as they can obtain from you.

Life skills are not restricted to clients, they are the vital ingredient for effective communication in everyday life.

What are life skills?

- being a 'natural' communicator
- demonstrating positive social behaviour
- being able to empathise with people (to relate to them)
- being knowledgeable in a variety of subjects related to life and living.

In a salon/establishment the entire staff should be working at developing these key skill areas for communicating with:

- each other
- clients
- the general public.

In this era everyone complains that:

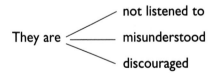

The simple solution is to develop a **more positive approach** so that people can feel:

- listened to
- understood
- encouraged.

This is the basic or foundation level for your life skills to develop and grow from.

You will need to be **receptive** to other peoples **needs** and **feelings** so that if and when clients wish to share personal problems with you, you can offer empathy and demonstrate a professional (objective) manner, but this shouldn't mean that your approach is detached or uninterested.

It does mean that you offer:

- a listening ear
- knowledgeable constructive comments if required.

But it does also mean that you should not become personally involved with the situation (subjectivity). You personally have **no** involvement and should not attempt to involve yourself. You should merely listen to your client's situation.

Listening skills

Many people think that listening skills are something difficult, hard to learn, complicated. They **are not**. They are **simple** – you just listen to your client or colleague. The difficult part is doing it – **listening**.

Often a client will just want to tell you about her/his situation or feelings about a particular topic.

It may be a **family crisis**:

- divorce   • separation   • bereavement

It may be a personal problem:

- redundancy • miscarriage • abortion • depression • obesity

It may be an **external problem** the client is concerned about:

- a world problem – war
- a national problem
- pollution

Sometimes clients will want to discuss problems or feelings that are particularly suited to their age range. Often this means that they are wanting to be **reassured** that these 'problems' or feelings are normal.

The skill and knowledge of the therapist are required in quite a wide range of topics. Naturally, acquiring these skills takes time but they are necessary in your work.

Frequently clients say they prefer a more mature therapist and this is because they feel that the therapists will be able to understand them more easily. This, of course, is not always true, but what it does suggest is that therapists need to **acquire and develop life skills very early in their training** if in the salon environment they are going to be able to assist a wide age range of clients.

In considering the age of the client it is also important to remember that the **male** client is now a regular attender of beauty establishments. Dealing with the male should not be so different from dealing with the female client.

The therapist must always maintain:

- a professional manner in attitude, voice, dress
- an objective approach (never a personal involvement).

Then there is no cause for misinterpretation of language or gestures.

The male client may also wish to discuss various topics with the therapist so it is important to have an equal understanding of both male and female lives.

Your female client is thinking of divorcing her husband and asks your opinion on what to do.   Explain your answer to her.

CHAPTER 26 *Problems to cope with*

So, what are the problems that affect people during their lifespan?

They are numerous but here is a selection taken from discussions with different clients.

Pre-twenties/adolescence
lack of self confidence/self esteem
physical appearance
weight
premenstrual tension
stress
fitness
need to be assertive
need to demonstrate manhood
need to identify with peer group
problems which cause personal anxiety (phobias)

Early adult
pre and post pregnancy
depression
premenstrual tension
dependence on alcohol or drugs
ego building
need to be assertive
disfigurement

Middle years
depression
premenopause
dependence on alcohol or drugs
stress
work
home
need to remain youthful
need to be attractive to the opposite sex

Mature adult
stress
family problems
tiredness and understanding change in body's performance
postmenopause
post-operative conditions
changes in male ego
changes in physical appearance

It can be important to be able to **identify** the problem with the **age group** so that you can assist if necessary with:

- reassurance
- empathy
- encouragement
- confidence.

However, some problems can occur at any age.

Depression

Many people seek medical advice for depression but a considerable number never receive help. The therapist can often be the person who recognises the client's depression and can be of great assistance in understanding or suggesting places to go for help.

Most of us at some time 'feel depressed' and we say so. This is important because we recognise how we are feeling; usually the 'depression' is temporary and we soon feel ourselves again.

But what about more serious depression that lingers on and on when the individual feels that life just isn't worth living because of this continual state of melancholia?

The medical profession tells us that there are two types of depression:

- exogenous, and
- endogenous.

EXOGENOUS DEPRESSION

This is the type of depression that occurs as a result of outside factors. These could be:

death of a close person
↓
divorce
↓
redundancy
↓
financial problems

ENDOGENOUS DEPRESSION

This is the type of depression that occurs as a result of internal biochemical sources, a biological form of depression.

It shows itself as periods of
↓
euphoria and
↓
hyperactivity

alternating with
↓
periods of deep depression

Clinical depression is a complex illness. It can go undetected because symptoms of anxiety may hide a deeper depression.

THE FACTS

- Depression is more common among women than men.
- Depression affects people of **all ages** from children to mature people.
- It is the cause of over 60% of suicides in the United Kingdom.

The therapist's understanding of depression is a valuable asset in her/his working life.

RECOGNISE THE SYMPTOMS. THEY CAN BE:

PSYCHOLOGICAL

loss of interest
↓
feeling low
↓
sense of despair
↓
guilty thoughts
↓
no enjoyment
↓
irritability
↓
suicidal thoughts
↓
poor concentration

OR THEY CAN BE:

PHYSICAL

loss of appetite
↓
weight loss
↓
no energy
↓
waking early
↓
waking in the 'middle' of the night
↓
low sex drive
↓
aches and pains
↓
general tiredness and apathy

FURTHER INFORMATION

Health Education Council, Hamilton House, Mabledon Place, London WC1H 9TX.

Your local Community Health Centre.

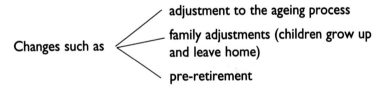

Anna is depressed and on medication. She has come for a massage because she hopes it might 'do her good'.	Outline your approach to Anna. What will you talk about? What lifestyle, homecare suggestions will you make?

Mid-life crisis

Psychologists Bee and Mitchell (1980) tell us that in any society there are particular ages when a number of stressful life changes, i.e. biological, social and psychological, are likely to take place.

These changes are a part of our personal development.

WHAT DOES THIS MEAN FOR THE INDIVIDUAL IN MID-LIFE?

For most people it means the normal adjustment to changes with little or no stress.

For others it means not coping or accepting changes which cause stress:

Changes such as
- adjustment to the ageing process
- family adjustments (children grow up and leave home)
- pre-retirement

The crises occur when a series of quite normal changes become too stressful for the person to deal with. Normal situations become out of proportion.

In a more relaxed state the individual can often:

- see the situation more clearly
- cope with the problem by accepting it.

Many clients value effective salon treatments as an alternative to seeking medical or other professional assistance at this time.

It is very important that the therapist is able to recognise this mid-life situation in her/his clientele.

MID-LIFE CRISIS – FEMALE

The female mid-life crisis is often associated with the **biological menopause**.

It is obvious that the physical and mental aspects will have an effect on the woman. How the individual goes through it is largely down to her and her mental attitude.

There are a variety of factors that will affect a woman:

Personal → emotional worries about ageing, loss of femininity
→ the need to remain attractive to the opposite sex
Work → this may be demanding, particularly if the job is a high-pressure career. Emotional upsets caused by hormone disturbance can lead to a lack of confidence, or an inability to cope
Family → pressures from home may still be demanding, although most children will now have reached adulthood
→ husbands/partners can add to pressure – they can also relieve it

Frequently the emotions are in a somewhat unbalanced state and evaluating one's life at mid-life can be either encouraging or disappointing.

Some women look back with **regret**.

They may have had:

- dreams
- high hopes.

They may not have achieved their goals or ideals and can become resentful in their attitude towards:

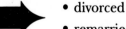

- colleagues
- friends
- their family.

Changes in personal relationships may have taken place.

The woman might be:

- divorced
- remarried
- a widow.

The emotions attached to a new, existing or changing relationship are varied and challenging at any age. These can be more apparent and difficult to cope with in mid-life (see Menopause/Stress charts on pages 196–9).

The woman who isn't actively involved in work outside of the home environment may experience a variety of emotions.

THE KEY ONE IS OFTEN 'FEELING OF USELESSNESS'.

- Her family may have grown up and are independent of her.
- Her partner may have work demands of his own that means he neglects to understand her feelings.
- Time can seem endless if her friends are working.

This is a good opportunity for her **to take up new interests/hobbies**.

- Adult day centres offer a variety of interesting classes.
- Local clubs may be just what she needs to develop herself and make new friends.

Medical help support groups exist for women who find the biological problems too much to cope with.

Mental attitude is of great importance and seeing life as a progressive journey with new challenges is the only way to proceed.

A positive outlook is helped by:

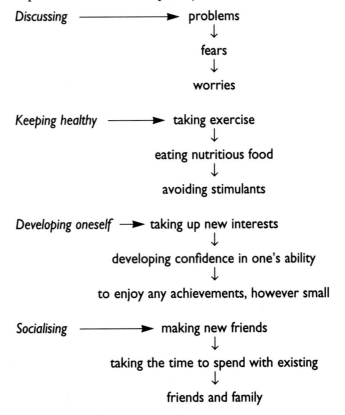

Discussing ⟶ problems
↓
fears
↓
worries

Keeping healthy ⟶ taking exercise
↓
eating nutritious food
↓
avoiding stimulants

Developing oneself ⟶ taking up new interests
↓
developing confidence in one's ability
↓
to enjoy any achievements, however small

Socialising ⟶ making new friends
↓
taking the time to spend with existing
↓
friends and family

The therapist's role with the mid-life client is supportive:

- listening
- encouraging

- promoting a good environment for the client to value herself.

Helping a client to **develop self-esteem** is a rewarding part of the therapist's work.

Many clients will seek all sorts of beauty treatments during this phase of their life.

You may have the opportunity to smooth their journey through mid-life.

MALE MID-LIFE CRISIS

Men experience problems related to mid-life.

Consider the sport enthusiast
If a male has been a keen sportsman the decline in his personal performance can be hard to accept, particularly if his associates are younger. This causes stress.

Consider health
A male who has enjoyed good health suddenly gets minor illnesses. There is often a tendency to magnify the illness because he feels vulnerable, having not previously experienced ill-health.

Consider work

Work challenges may seem difficult
↓
It may be harder to reach the goals
↓
Younger, energetic associates might appear more successful
↓
Advancing age may restrict promotion
↓
Redundancy may become a real threat

Consider homelife
Often wives or partners have resumed their careers and are busy and successful. This means that men sometimes feel neglected.

Sometimes it means that the male feels he must look elsewhere for female contact. The subconscious desire to be younger means that the male may try to establish relationships with younger women.

Occasionally decisions are made in haste and family life is affected. The escape to a younger woman, away from financial and family/partner commitments can seem appealing, but often this is only temporary. The real problems that may follow are

- divorce
- financial insecurity

because of the new situation.

The male ego does not like threats . . .

- redundancy
- growing older

are threats that will pose problems.

The male will often display many symptoms of mid-life crisis. Here are a few:

- worries about appearance
- competitiveness with younger men
- dissatisfaction with job
- lack of achievement
- lack of personal drive
- sexual drive can be under- or over-activated.

The real problem is the **mental attitude** towards all of the situations. Financial security cannot give psychological security.

The mid-life man needs to **look forward** to life as a **challenge** – not look back.

- A man can develop new interests, some on his own, some with his partner.
- He can create/develop a new image for his mid-life rather than try to regain a former one.

He needs to keep his **homelife** and **worklife** in perspective to enjoy the situations he is in and not allow situations that might never happen (e.g. redundancy) to cause unnecessary anxiety.

Maintaining a good self-image is a vital factor in sailing through the challenges posed by mid-life.

Salon treatments can assist in maintaining and developing the image and keeping the individual relaxed and able to cope with daily life.

1 Andy suffers with physical stress and has a sauna and back massage once a fortnight.

Although he is only 38 he feels that life is passing quickly and he is being left behind. He is becoming increasingly more concerned about this each time he visits the salon.

Outline some suggestions you might talk over with him to assist this problem or suggest some places he could go for further help.

2 Make a list of addresses that you feel might be useful to have as a working therapist when your clients ask you for information.

TALK ABOUT MID-LIFE CRISIS

Two clients, husband and wife (both in their early fifties) talk about their mid-life crises.

Marion I haven't really thought about a mid-life crisis. My family are grown up and married with children. There's no immediate worry about them.

I'm being made redundant, but this is not a problem to me as financially I will be all right as I am able to draw my pension. I might miss work, but I'll see how things go.

Menopause has affected me in some way. I have had hot flushes and I'm now taking HRT – hormone replacement therapy.

Naturally no-one wants to get old and we all want to look young but then I have had facials and body massage for several years and more recently I've started to have reflexology, so I have tried to look after myself.

Arthur and I eat a reasonably balanced diet and we drink lots of water, so we think about our bodies, although we don't take a lot of exercise.

I suppose the only thing that does worry me is the thought of developing osteoporosis/osteo-arthritis. My mother suffers with this and so did my grandmother. I wouldn't like to get older and be affected by this. It's nice to grow older and still be fit. Still, I'm taking HRT and this will help my bones, so I am told.

Really, I don't feel any older so I don't think of myself as being in mid-life. I think it is one's state of mind a lot of the time. Arthur and I like to enjoy our grandchildren so it's important to stay young for them.

Arthur I think my mid-life crisis has been the collapse of my business. When I was younger I always wanted my own business, but it never seemed to be the right time. Then in my early forties I took the plunge. Recession didn't help with the collapse of the building trade, so the business just folded.

I had achieved my goal but I hadn't been able to develop it. Then I had to find work; I was determined to find something and now I've got a job again.

I think being positive is important. You have your ups and downs but you have to get on with it. Marion and I try to look after ourselves. I've had a regular massage for years and more recently reflexology. I think it helps you to unwind.

Your middle aged female client is concerned about her facial skin which is red and dry and very lined. She is very upset at the thought of getting old and tells you that she regularly drowns her sorrows with double whiskies.

Explain how you will proceed with this client.

Stress

Stress is a natural part of living. Relatively simple tasks produce stress and some stress is necessary for us to meet changes and new situations.

The ability to deal with stress varies considerably from one person to another.

Successful, happy people have learned the secret of balancing their stress levels.

People under stress have been unable to adapt and their stress leads to further problems.

WHAT CAN CAUSE STRESS?

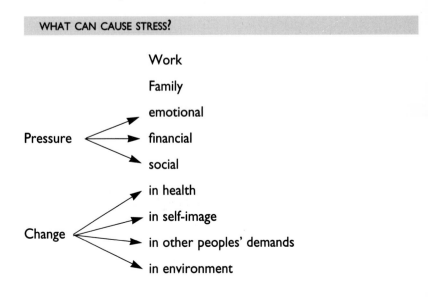

Work

Family

Pressure
- emotional
- financial
- social

Change
- in health
- in self-image
- in other peoples' demands
- in environment

THE EFFECTS OF STRESS ON THE BODY

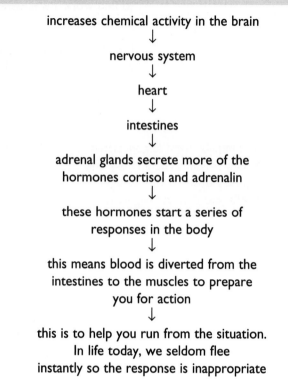

increases chemical activity in the brain
↓
nervous system
↓
heart
↓
intestines
↓
adrenal glands secrete more of the
hormones cortisol and adrenalin
↓
these hormones start a series of
responses in the body
↓
this means blood is diverted from the
intestines to the muscles to prepare
you for action
↓
this is to help you run from the situation.
In life today, we seldom flee
instantly so the response is inappropriate

Stress unchecked or handled negatively leads to further problems:

- palpitations
- diarrhoea
- constipation
- skin irritation
- sexual problems
- tension
- sleeplessness
- tiredness
- anxiety
- poor concentration
- illness
- disturbed eating habits
- alcohol and drug abuse
- obsessions

and ultimately the inability to cope with:

- relationships
- emotions
- work.

The individual has:

- a low self esteem
- a lack of fulfilment
- frequent depression

PEOPLE THAT COPE WITH STRESS LOOK AFTER THEIR PHYSICAL HEALTH

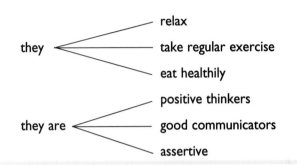

they
- relax
- take regular exercise
- eat healthily

they are
- positive thinkers
- good communicators
- assertive

MANY PEOPLE ARE ABLE TO RECOGNISE THAT THEY ARE SUFFERING WITH STRESS AND TAKE STEPS TO REDUCE THEIR OWN LEVEL

They ⟶ learn how to relax

make time for personal time

accept that only one job can be done at a time

discuss problems with a friend

start a sport or general exercise

take up a new hobby

learn to say no

Your salon has a monthly open evening when new and regular clients attend a social gathering. During the evening a young male client becomes extremely noisy and finally sits down in distress announcing that he's being made redundant at the end of the month.

Describe what you would do next.

A DIFFERENT KIND OF STRESS: POST-TRAUMATIC STRESS

This is an emotional condition. It occurs after a very disturbing event. This is usually outside the range of normal experience, e.g. a major disaster such as a train crash or war.

It can occur

- at any age
- at any time

Some people are more susceptible than others. Often they are people who have experienced trauma throughout their life and have a higher incidence of psychological problems.

Simple charts/scales can record stress levels and can help the individual in:

- assessing self
- measuring resistance to stress

The following charts are informative and constructive. Test your own stress levels and be aware of other colleagues or clients' stress levels.

REMEMBER

A stressed therapist cannot give the best treatment, so personal stress control is vital for harmony in the workplace.

TEST YOUR OWN STRESS LEVEL TESTS TO TEST YOUR STRESS LEVEL AND YOUR ABILITY TO COPE WITH STRESS

These tests are based on questionnaires developed by the American stress psychologists Lyle H. Miller and Alma Dell Smith of the University of Boston Medical Centre.

Test 1 measures the overall level of stress you are subject to at the moment,
Test 2 your ability to cope with it.

Source These tests appeared in the *Reader's Digest Guide to Alternative Medicine*

Test 1: Rate yourself for stress

The list on the right gives ten responses often made by people under pressure. Each response can be rated for stress from 1 (not stressful) to 5 (very stressful). If you can remember responding in any of these ways in the last six months, circle the number under the 'past' column that represents the amount of stress you experienced at the time. Under the 'future' column, circle numbers to represent the amount of stress you expect to experience from responses that may occur during the next six months. Add up both past and future scores, then add them together. A score over 30 indicates a potential stress problem, while more than 53 calls for a worked-out programme to fight stress.

Response	Past	Future
1 Depression	1 2 3 4 5	1 2 3 4 5
2 Frustration	1 2 3 4 5	1 2 3 4 5
3 Guilt	1 2 3 4 5	1 2 3 4 5
4 Anxiety or panic	1 2 3 4 5	1 2 3 4 5
5 Desperation or hopelessness	1 2 3 4 5	1 2 3 4 5
6 Feeling out of control	1 2 3 4 5	1 2 3 4 5
7 Selfconsciousness	1 2 3 4 5	1 2 3 4 5
8 Irritation and anger	1 2 3 4 5	1 2 3 4 5
9 Restlessness	1 2 3 4 5	1 2 3 4 5
10 Feeling trapped or helpless	1 2 3 4 5	1 2 3 4 5

Test 2: Measure your resistance

This test measures how much your way of life supports you and bolsters resistance to stress. Rate yourself for each of the 20 items on the scale from 1 (almost always) to 5 (never) according to how often they apply.

Add up your total score. A score of 45 or less shows high resistance to stress and a healthy way of life; 45 to 55 indicates that you may be susceptible to the effects of stress and could benefit from adjusting certain aspects of your daily life; over 55 and stress could be a serious risk, calling for a reappraisal of your general way of life.

How much of the time are these statements true for you?	Almost always	Most times	Some- times	Rarely	Never
1 My health is good (including eyesight, teeth, etc.)	1	2	3	4	5
2 My income meets my basic expenses	1	2	3	4	5
3 I am about the right weight for my build and height	1	2	3	4	5
4 I give and receive affection regularly	1	2	3	4	5
5 I express my feelings when angry or worried	1	2	3	4	5
6 I have fewer than three caffeine-containing drinks (coffee, cocoa or cola) a day	1	2	3	4	5
7 I take part in regular social activities	1	2	3	4	5
8 I eat at least one full, well-balanced meal a day	1	2	3	4	5
9 I do something just for pleasure at least once a week	1	2	3	4	5
10 There is at least one relative within 50 miles (80 km) of home on whom I can rely	1	2	3	4	5
11 I have some time alone during the day	1	2	3	4	5
12 I get seven or eight hours of sleep at least four nights a week	1	2	3	4	5
13 My religious beliefs give me strength	1	2	3	4	5
14 I exercise hard enough to work up a sweat at least twice a week	1	2	3	4	5
15 I have a network of friends and acquaintances	1	2	3	4	5
16 I discuss problems such as housework and money with other members of the household	1	2	3	4	5
17 I have at least one friend I can talk to about personal affairs	1	2	3	4	5
18 I smoke no more than 10 cigarettes a day	1	2	3	4	5
19 I organise my time well	1	2	3	4	5
20 I have fewer than five alcoholic drinks a week	1	2	3	4	5

USEFUL ADDRESSES:

Health Education Authority, Hamilton House, Mabledon Place, London WC1H 9TX.

Your local Community Health Centre or your GP.

A regular client in her thirties tells you of her recent escape from a fatal road accident. She is now suffering from post-traumatic stress and feels very insecure and uncertain.

Outline your approach to treatment and any suggestions that you might make.

STRESS AND ILLNESS

In the 1970s stress experts Thomas Holmes and Richard Rahe found that stress due to important life changes was an accurate predictor of future illness.

They made a table of 43 possible changes and rated each one for stressfulness on a scale from one to 100.

To rate yourself on the scale, add up the scores for all the events listed that you have experienced during the last year.

A total of 150 gives a 50 per cent chance of a health change occurring in the near future and a total of *over 300* gives a 90 per cent chance, unless effective measures are taken to reduce the stress level.

Death of spouse	100
Divorce	73
Marital separation	65
Jail term	63
Death of close family member	63
Personal injury or illness	53
Marriage	50
Loss of job	47
Marital reconciliation	45
Retirement	45
Change in health of family member	44
Pregnancy	40
Sexual problems	39
Gain of new family member	39
Business readjustment	39

Change in financial state 38
Death of close friend 37
Change to different type of work 36
Change in number of arguments with spouse 35
High mortgage 31
Foreclosure of mortgage or loan 30
Change in responsibilities at work 29
Son or daughter leaving home 29
Trouble with in-laws 29
Outstanding personal achievement 29
Spouse begins or stops work 26
Beginning or ending education 26
Change in living conditions 25
Changed personal habits 24
Trouble with boss 23
Change in working hours or conditions 20
Moving house 20
Changing schools 20
Change in leisure pursuits 19
Change in church activities 19
Change in social activities 18
Low to medium mortgage or loan 17
Altered sleeping habits 16
Change in number of family get-togethers 15
Change in eating habits 15
Going on holiday 13
Approaching Christmas season 12
Minor violations of the law 11

You can also use the index to predict and plan changes in the future such as moving house or starting a new job so that stressful events do not all happen at once or build up to a crisis.

Design a stress evaluation test that you would use yourself to regularly monitor your stress levels.

a) Test it on a colleague.

b) Make a list of possible recommendations to reduce your stress level/someone else's stress level.

Myalgic Encephalomyelitis (ME)

Many ME sufferers are encouraged by the medical profession to seek relaxing massage, aromatherapy and reflexology to help this condition. Any treatment that assists the immune system is valuable. It is helpful for the therapist to have a broad comprehension of ME in order to be able to understand clients' problems.

What is ME?

Myalgic Encephalomyelitis literally means inflammation of the brain and the spinal cord with associated muscular pain.

The medical profession originally classified it as psychological. It is now recognised as a physical illness although there are some doctors that do not accept this classification.

It is more commonly associated with Post Viral Fatigue Syndrome (PVFS), as there appears to be some link with the sufferer being unable to recover fully from a virus.

Medical research has shown many *disorders* in sufferers but they are not always peculiar to each sufferer and blood tests do not always confirm the presence of a virus. Researchers are unable, therefore, to state the cause.

The symptoms

- extreme fatigue following a virus, i.e. the smallest exertion can weaken muscles for several days
- muscular pains
- generally unwell
- visual disturbances – headaches
- ringing in the ears – earache
- swollen glands
- fever – hot and cold flushes
- persistent skin rashes
- stomach complaints – nausea
- insomnia
- chest pains
- depression – mood swings and temporary inability to concentrate
- loss of memory
- bladder problems

WHO CAN BE AFFECTED?

The condition can affect anyone but it is particularly prominent among people in their 20s and 30s.

Active, successful people appear to be one group who are most affected.

People who have had trauma and either physical or emotional stress.

THE TREATMENT

Medically if certain organs have been affected treatment can be prescribed. Anti-depressants are given to some sufferers but the main healing element is **time**.

The sufferer is encouraged to have

- a varied diet and vitamin supplement
- plenty of rest
- light exercise

Complementary therapies can have success in restoring some vitality for the sufferer. **Acupuncture, aromatherapy and reflexology** are often recommended to sufferers. The illness has many symptoms but not every sufferer has all of them. Chronic fatigue is the one factor common to all. The sufferer will have bouts of the symptoms and every day can be different.

The disorder can last for many months and, in some severe cases, years.

ME is now classified as a neurological disease by the World Health Organisation and the Department of Health Disability and Living Allowance Board.

FURTHER INFORMATION:

ME Association, Stanhope House, High Street, Stanford le Hope, Essex SS17 8EX.
Tel: (01375) 642466

Your client has been suffering for a long time from post-viral fatigue syndrome. She is concerned about the different problems she has and whether they are associated with the disorder. She wants uplifting treatments and a 'magic' cure.

Explain how you will proceed.

Anorexia nervosa

The number of young people diagnosed as suffering with anorexia nervosa has doubled in each decade over the last 30 years (Richards, 1982).

WHAT IS IT?

Anorexia is a steady loss of weight associated with compulsive dieting. If left untreated, the condition can be fatal.

WHAT CAUSES IT?

A number of factors have been found that appear to cause anorexia. Dieting itself is not the cause but it does act as a trigger.

- It is more common in females than males
- It is more common in the 16 to 19 year age range
- A person may start dieting to lose a few pounds and then find the results so rewarding that the main aim becomes to lose weight. Self-starvation becomes satisfying and all the individual's efforts are channelled into losing weight. Everything else loses its meaning
- Parental pressures to achieve at school or college/university
- Pressures in the home environment

     ↓

  hostility towards parent(s)

     ↓

  change or disruption in family relationships

     ↓

  history of psychiatric illness in the family

- Anorexics all have a distorted view of themselves:
  - they avoid situations they fear
  - they believe they look and are greatly overweight
  - they have obsessive personalities
  - they have low self-esteem
  - they are unable to manage their own lives.

Many anorexics starve themselves so much that they then 'crave' food and go on a binge of eating. They then make themselves vomit so as not to gain weight.

This condition is called **secondary anorexia** or **bulimia nervosa.**

The biological effect of anorexia and bulimia on the body is similar to that of malnutrition:

- wasting of muscles
- weakening of the heart
- cessation of menstruation
- poor skin and hair
- physical weakness.

The therapist needs to be very aware of the anorexic client who needs support and understanding to ensure that the correct salon treatment is given.

FURTHER INFORMATION:

Eating Disorders Association, Sackville Place, 44 Magdalen Street, Norwich, Norfolk NR3 1JU.
Tel: (01603) 621414

A young, very slim, client is repeatedly asking you for a reducing diet.

How will you assess the situation and give her the best advice?

Bereavement – grief

Death – particularly the death of people that we are close to – causes a great deal of trauma for the individual. People cope with the loss in different ways. Mourning can last a short time or for several years.

Some people:

- continue to work hard to try and forget
- rely on medication to assist them
- can become ill.

Whatever happens for the individual, we know that grief is a normal process and essential for psychological and physical well-being.

People who grieve **need**:

- to talk to share their feelings
- comfort
- support by relatives and friends
- a good listener.

Sometimes the bereaved person prefers to talk to someone outside of the family because that person is detached from the situation.

It is not always necessary to say anything to the person, rather to present the 'right' environment so that the person feels comfortable and wants to share their thoughts and feelings.

It means that the listener's body language and attitude is saying 'you are allowed
- to grieve
- to remember the person
- to shed feelings of guilt and uncertainty
- to remember the good and the bad times'
and '*I am willing to listen.*'

Some people's loss is so great and it affects their life so deeply that they may need continual support. Knowing where to go for help is always useful and in many areas local community care services operate a counselling service for the bereaved.

A useful address for more information on bereavement counsellors is:

CRUSE, Bereavement Care, Cruse House, 126 Sheen Road, Richmond, Surrey TW9 1UR.

Other forms of loss

Another form of 'mourning' for some women is the loss of part of their body:

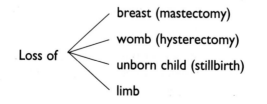

A **mastectomy** or a **hysterectomy** can leave a woman feeling 'less of a woman'. Her confidence takes a plunge as she knows that she can never have that part of her body again. Physically, her hormones may be unsettled for a long period of time.

Some clients who have had a mastectomy may use a prosthesis. Careful and considerate handling of the client is vital to avoid any embarrassment.

A **stillbirth** is a 'death'. The client's emotions will take time to readjust to what has happened. This can be a very slow process for some women. The client will often benefit by talking to a therapist. Frequently there are feelings that are not discussed. Aromatherapy treatments will often affect the release of this type of emotion.

The **loss of a limb** will be traumatic at any time. Today the use of a prosthesis can be a great help to the individual but the client still has to come to terms with the situation.

The therapist's skill in client care and handling is very important.

- Knowing **when to be there**, and **when not to be there** is crucial for your client's well-being.

Some clients will show no embarrassment and may even ask you to assist them with, for example, their artificial leg.

REMEMBER

- don't stare
- don't be shocked
- relax and wait for your client to ask for help.

Other clients are embarrassed and may not even tell you during the consultation. If the opportunity arises it may be easier for you to ask tactfully; here is an actual client example taken during consultation:

Client: I've had a mastectomy.
Therapist: Does this cause you any problems?
Client: It used to worry me but not now I have this special bra. Would you like to see it?

The therapist, of course, responded to this in the affirmative and the client felt at ease and reassured because of the therapist's positive reaction.

Always observe how the client:

- stands
- moves

- walks

- sits.

Body movements will help you to notice problem regions before you speak to your client.

REMEMBER

- there are many other forms of loss that are equally important to the client

Loss of
- job (redundancy)
- home (forced to move)

Today counselling is being offered to individuals more freely, before and after a situation such as mastectomy.

A woman needs time to come to terms with the situation and often wants to talk about her feelings and other people's feelings towards her, e.g. those of her partner.

Understanding and reassurance in this situation are the basis of the client's security.

Similarly, counsellors are available to assist people who are forced to take redundancy or who suffer a major upheaval in their life. Being aware of your client's feelings can greatly assist your client-handling skills. Your professional relationship with your client will also be firmly established and your client will value your professional service and expertise.

Other life problems

PREMENSTRUAL TENSION (PMT)

More and more women are affected by premenstrual tension. The 'tension' presents itself with a variety of symptoms which can last for two or three days or up to two weeks before a period.

Most of the symptoms are not dangerous but the distress and upset that they cause the individual can be quite traumatic.

There are two types of symptoms:

Physical   water retention – swollen hands, ankles, face
cravings for chocolate, alcohol
violent temper
headaches
swollen joints
nausea

skin and hair problems

Psychological   irritability
insomnia
depression
poor concentration
mood changes
irrational behaviour

WHAT IS PREMENSTRUAL TENSION?

It is a change in the hormonal balance during the menstrual cycle which causes salt and water to build up. There is also a shortage of the hormone progesterone.

TREATMENT

Two common treatments are:

- vitamin B6: which can assist in regulating the menstrual cycle
- linoleic acid: an essential fatty acid which is vital for maintaining the delicate hormone balance.

Aromatherapy and reflexology treatments are known to assist premenstrual tension in helping the body to normalise.

MENOPAUSE, OR 'CHANGE OF LIFE'

This is one of the most common complaints for women. Menopause can display a variety of ailments and problems and women may suffer from only one or two, or a wide range of problems.

WHAT IS IT?

It is the permanent ending of periods: ovaries stop producing eggs and fertility declines and eventually ceases.

Menopause usually occurs from the mid forties but some women are younger. The menopause usually takes two or three years. During this time the ovaries reduce in size and finally stop producing eggs. The hormone oestrogen, which maintains the female reproductive system and keeps a woman feeling fit and well and contributes to the condition of many organs of the body, also stops being produced.

In some women the menstrual cycle stops suddenly. Others find it becomes irregular with longer gaps between periods. Some may experience very heavy bleeding.

Loss of oestrogen causes:

- hot flushes
- night sweats
- vaginal dryness
- greater need to urinate.

These problems can cause great distress for the person not only through embarrassment but through a genuine feeling of being unwell. Hot flushes can be mild or severe. There can be a feeling of warmth from head to toe as body temperature rises and falls. A woman can appear bright red and dripping with perspiration. For some women hormone replacement therapy (HRT) has helped these problems (see page 192).

Some women appear to suffer many problems, others only a few. There are a variety of problems associated with the menopause:

Emotional

irritability
↓
anxiety
↓
lack of concentration
↓
mood swings
↓
depression
↓
migraine

Physical problems

skin (unbalanced, dry, irritated, sensitive)
↓
nails (brittle)
↓
weight gain and water retention
↓
hair (loss of colour, dry, change in texture)
↓
vaginal infections/dryness
↓
irregular sleeping pattern

Psychological problems related to

feelings of getting old
↓
looking unattractive
↓
being middle-aged
↓
loss of confidence

These problems are very real to the person. The menopausal client often needs reassurance, patience, understanding and belief in herself. She needs to accept the changes her body is going through.

Salon treatments can help the client look better and feel better. They are a great boost to the morale. The menopausal woman will also benefit from:

- a balanced diet
- regular exercise, such as walking or swimming.

POSTMENOPAUSE

Once the menopausal years have passed a woman feels different. Certain problems have been removed:

- no more periods
- no pregnancy worries
- no need for contraception.

The average woman is still active and may enjoy sport or exercise. The body appears to settle down and most of the early problems disappear.

A female client in her fifties has a variety of problems which she feels are related to the menopause. She wants your help but finishes her sentence with '... you're far too young to understand what I am going through'.

Explain how you can reassure this client.

MIGRAINE

This is a very common problem and affects people in different ways. Clients who suffer with migraine will benefit from the relaxing treatments that are available in the beauty establishment.

Relaxation is always helpful. Some migraine is particularly stress related. Body massage, aromatherapy and reflexology are all treatments which help the body to harmonise and regulate itself.

Clients often want to talk about the problem and are pleased to know if you have come across other sufferers. It offers them a form of reassurance.

WHAT IS MIGRAINE?

Migraine is a severe recurrent painful headache. It is usually situated at the front of the head on one side only. It produces a hammering/throbbing pain.

Migraine sufferers will often have one or more symptoms, such as visual disturbances, aversion to light.

WHAT CAUSES MIGRAINE?

There are a variety of things that tend to trigger attacks, for example:

* smells – perfume
* food – chocolate

Often an attack can occur when the person relaxes. Many migraine sufferers get an attack at the weekend after a busy week at work.

DRUGS

Certain drugs have been associated with migraine:

* the contraceptive pill
* hormone replacement therapy
* drugs associated with high blood pressure.

FURTHER INFORMATION:

The British Migraine Association, 178A High Road, Byfleet, Surrey, KT14 7ED.
(No telephone)

The Migraine Trust, 45 Great Ormond Street, London WC1N 3HD.

PHOBIAS

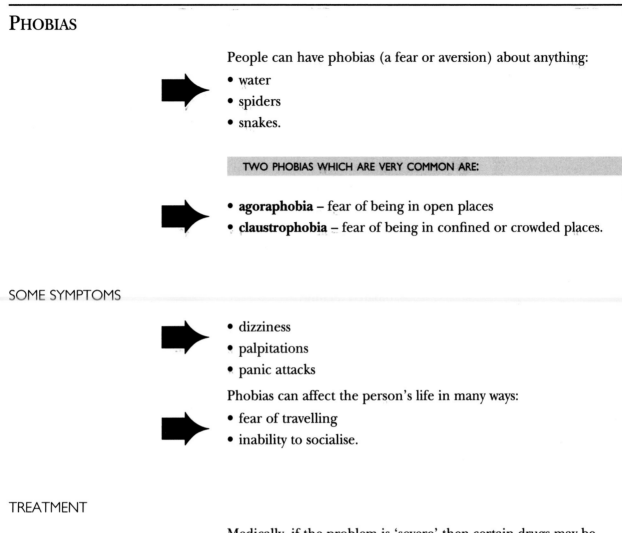

People can have phobias (a fear or aversion) about anything:

- water
- spiders
- snakes.

> TWO PHOBIAS WHICH ARE VERY COMMON ARE:

- **agoraphobia** – fear of being in open places
- **claustrophobia** – fear of being in confined or crowded places.

SOME SYMPTOMS

- dizziness
- palpitations
- panic attacks

Phobias can affect the person's life in many ways:

- fear of travelling
- inability to socialise.

TREATMENT

Medically, if the problem is 'severe' then certain drugs may be prescribed or the individual can be recommended for psychotherapy or psychiatry. Self-help groups exist for individual support.

Many people's phobias are mild and never get out of hand. Talking freely about them assists the problem.

The therapist may never come across deep-rooted phobias because the client does not reveal them.

IRRITABLE BOWEL SYNDROME (IBS)

This condition is often also referred to as **mucous colitis** or **spastic colon**.

WHAT IS IT?

Irritable bowel syndrome prevents the contraction and relaxation of the rings of muscle in the walls of the gut which push downwards through the intestines into the colon, rectum and to the anus.

If this muscle action is weak or disturbed spasmodic pain occurs with mucous diarrhoea or constipation. These symptoms can alternate. Bowel muscles are controlled by the autonomic nervous system, i.e. they are not consciously controlled.

SYMPTOMS

- mucous diarrhoea/constipation
- crampy pains in lower abdomen
- wind
- bloated feelings
- lethargy/back pain

Irritable bowel syndrome can be aggravated by nervous problems such as anxiety and stress.

Irritable bowel syndrome can also be caused by a severe infection in the intestines.

Aromatherapy and reflexology treatments can help this condition.

Reference section

CHAPTER 27 *Figure faults*

Postural disorders

SPINAL CURVATURE – TYPES

- *Kyphosis* – thoracic part of the spine curves outward.
  Causes: tight pectoral muscles, round shoulders.
- *Scoliosis* – lateral curvature to the right or left.
  Causes:

changes to
- muscles
- ligaments
- bones and joints

Long-term effects of scoliosis:

- scapulae uneven
- shoulders uneven
- pelvic tilt
- one leg shorter than the other
- *Lordosis* – inward curvature of the spine in the lumbar area often linked with forward tilt of the pelvis.

These conditions require medical approval before giving treatments or exercise routines.

Figure analysis

BODY TYPES

Mesomorph
- strong
- broad shoulders
- well-toned muscles
- active (athletic type)
- weight usually maintained while active

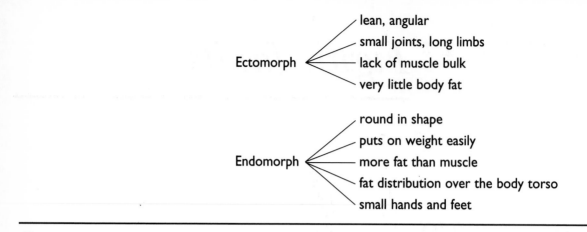

Ectomorph
- lean, angular
- small joints, long limbs
- lack of muscle bulk
- very little body fat

Endomorph
- round in shape
- puts on weight easily
- more fat than muscle
- fat distribution over the body torso
- small hands and feet

CORRECT POSTURE

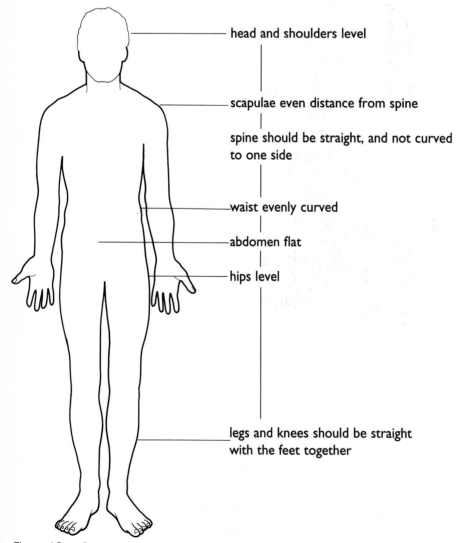

- head and shoulders level
- scapulae even distance from spine
- spine should be straight, and not curved to one side
- waist evenly curved
- abdomen flat
- hips level
- legs and knees should be straight with the feet together

Figure 18:   *Correct posture*

Diet

The purpose of food

builds body tissues
|
supplies the body with energy
|
regulates body processes

The composition of food

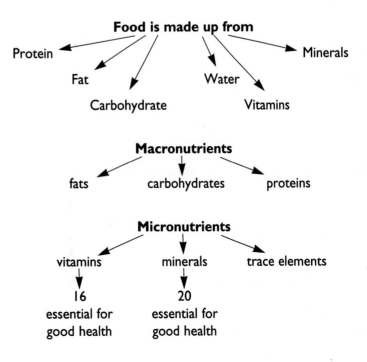

Vitamins, their functions and deficiency symptoms

Vitamin	Function	Deficiency symptom
Vitamin A	Essential for normal growth, healthy eyes and night vision, maintenance of healthy skin and mucous membranes and immune responses.	Increased susceptibility to bacterial infection, skin changes, night blindness
Vitamin B1	Controls conversion of carbohydrate foods to energy. Essential for growth, normal appetite, digestion and healthy nerves.	Mental confusion, muscle fatigue, emotional instability, depression, loss of appetite, beri-beri
Vitamin B2	Essential for growth, health of eyes and for digestion. Involved in formation of thyroid enzyme regulating activities.	Soreness of lips, mouth and tongue; loss of visual acuity
Vitamin B3	Helps to control the release of energy from protein, fat and carbohydrate, i.e. the three main components that make up food.	Muscular weakness, loss of appetite, indigestion, skin lesions, pellagra (dermatitis, dementia, diarrhoea)
Vitamin B6	Required for metabolism of protein (meat, fish, eggs, etc.). Essential in formation of sheath surrounding nerve cells. Involved in immune system.	Depression, nausea, irritability, change in alertness
Vitamin B12	Essential for normal functioning of all body cells, especially for those of the nervous system and bone marrow. Promotes production of red blood cells.	Pernicious anaemia, degeneration of nerve endings
Folic acid	Essential for formation of red and white blood cells in bone marrow, and for their maturation.	Poor growth, anaemia and other blood disorders
Vitamin C	Multiple functions involved at enzyme level. Essential in formation of collagen in fibrous tissues such as cartilage, connective tissue and skin. Promotes healing of wounds, fractures and bleeding gums. Reduces liability to infection.	Poor appetite and growth, anaemia, inflamed gums, failure of wounds to heal, depression
Vitamin D	Essential for growth and development of bones and teeth. Important role in maintaining appropriate levels of calcium and phosphorus in the blood to support mineralisation of bones.	Fragility of bones, rickets in children
Vitamin E	Not yet fully understood. Appears to protect cell membranes from deterioration.	Muscle weakness

Source: Doyle, W. (1994) *Teach Yourself Healthy Eating*, London: Hodder and Stoughton.

Vitamins and their sources

Vitamin	Synonym	Sources
A	Retinol	Fish liver oil, liver, kidney, dairy produce, margarine, egg yolks, yellow and dark green vegetables
B1	Thiamin	Yeast, wholemeal bread and cereals, lean pork and bacon, liver, nuts, milk, eggs, pulses and other vegetables
B2	Riboflavin	Milk, liver, eggs, cheese, wholemeal bread and cereals, green vegetables
B3	Niacin	Meat, fish, wholemeal bread and cereals, pulses, nuts, yeast and meat extracts
B6	Pyridoxine	Liver, kidney and other meats, wholemeal cereals, nuts, seeds, bananas, fish
B12	Cyanocobalamin	Liver, kidney, oily fish, eggs, cheese and milk
	Folic acid	Liver, kidney, eggs, pulses, green vegetables, avocado pears, bananas, orange juice
C	Ascorbic acid	Citrus fruit, blackcurrants, rosehips, raw green vegetables, potatoes, tomatoes, strawberries
D	Calciferol	(Sunlight), oily fish, eggs, margarine, butter
E	Tocopherol	Wheatgerm, egg yolk, nuts, seeds and seed oils; margarines made from seed oils; green plants

Source: Doyle, W. (1994) *Teach Yourself Healthy Eating*, London: Hodder and Stoughton.

Reference Nutrient Intakes (RNIs) per day for selected nutrients

Males	Protein (g)	Vit. B1 (mg)	Vit. B2 (mg)	Niacin (mg)	Vit. B6 (mg)	Vit. B12 (mcg)	Folate (mcg)	Vit. C (mg)	Vit. A (mcg)	Calcium (mg)	Iron (mg)	Zinc (mg)
1–3 years	14.5	0.5	0.6	8	0.7	0.5	70	30	400	350	6.9	5.0
4–6 years	19.7	0.7	0.8	11	0.9	0.8	100	30	500	450	6.1	6.5
7–10 years	28.3	0.7	1.0	12	1.0	1.0	150	30	500	550	8.7	7.0
11–14 years	42.1	0.9	1.2	15	1.2	1.2	200	35	600	1000	11.3	9.0
15–18 years	55.2	1.1	1.3	18	1.5	1.5	200	40	700	1000	11.3	9.5
19–50 years	55.5	1.0	1.3	17	1.4	1.5	200	40	700	700	8.7	9.5
50+ years	53.3	0.9	1.3	16	1.4	1.5	200	40	700	700	8.7	9.5

Females	Protein (g)	Vit. B1 (mg)	Vit. B2 (mg)	Niacin (mg)	Vit. B6 (mg)	Vit. B12 (mcg)	Folate (mcg)	Vit. C (mg)	Vit. A (mcg)	Calcium (mg)	Iron (mg)	Zinc (mg)
1–3 years	14.5	0.5	0.6	8	0.7	0.5	70	30	400	350	6.9	5.0
4–6 years	19.7	0.7	0.8	11	0.9	0.8	100	30	500	450	6.1	6.5
7–10 years	28.3	0.7	1.0	12	1.0	1.0	150	30	500	550	8.7	7.0
11–14 years	41.2	0.7	1.1	12	1.0	1.2	200	35	600	800	14.8**	9.0
15–18 years	45.0	0.8	1.1	14	1.2	1.5	200	40	600	800	14.8**	7.0
19–50 years	45.0	0.8	1.1	13	1.2	1.5	200	40	600	700	14.8**	7.0
50+ years	46.5	0.8	1.1	12	1.2	1.5	200	40	600	700	8.7	7.0
Pregnancy	+6	+0.1*	+0.3	–	–	–	+100	+10	+100	–	–	–
Lactation												
0–4 months	+11	+0.2	+0.5	+2	–	+0.5	+60	+30	+350	+550	–	+6.0
4+ months	+8	+0.2	+0.5	+2	–	+0.5	+60	+30	+350	+550	–	+2.5

—   no increase
*   last trimester only
**   Insufficient for women with high menstrual losses

*Source: Dietary Reference Values for Food Energy and Nutrients for the United Kingdom, HMSO, London (1990).
Reproduced with the permission of the Controller, HMSO.*

The body's food requirements

The body's food requirements varies with:

• the age of the person
• the sex of the person.

The person with a low daily energy requirement of 1200 kilocalories needs food from all the basic food groups as much as a person with a high daily energy requirement of 3000 calories.

The **COMA Report** in 1984 (DHSS Committee on the Medical Aspects of Food Policy) reported that in order to maintain good health we should:

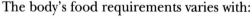

• reduce fat intake, especially saturated fat
• restrict salty and sugary foods
• eat fibre-rich foods such as wholemeal bread, cereals, brown rice, fruit and vegetables
• drink only 'moderate' amounts of alcohol.

THE BODY'S FOOD REQUIREMENTS AND WEIGHT CONTROL

Weight control should be achieved by controlling certain types of food such as sugary food, and balancing the nutritional content of food with energy output.

Sources of protein

From animal sources (a good source of essential amino acids)
  meat, fish, eggs, milk and cheese

From vegetable and cereal sources
  pulses (lentils, soya beans, chick peas, kidney beans, dried beans and peas)
  bread, wheat products
  nuts and seeds

Each of these sources is low in one or more of the essential amino acids and should therefore be eaten in combination with others to ensure the correct balance.

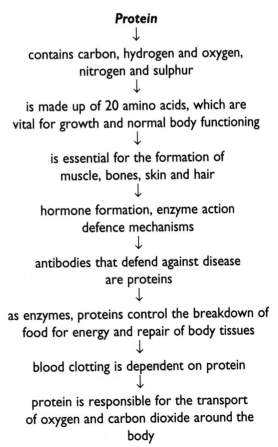

Protein
↓
contains carbon, hydrogen and oxygen,
nitrogen and sulphur
↓
is made up of 20 amino acids, which are
vital for growth and normal body functioning
↓
is essential for the formation of
muscle, bones, skin and hair
↓
hormone formation, enzyme action
defence mechanisms
↓
antibodies that defend against disease
are proteins
↓
as enzymes, proteins control the breakdown of
food for energy and repair of body tissues
↓
blood clotting is dependent on protein
↓
protein is responsible for the transport
of oxygen and carbon dioxide around the
body

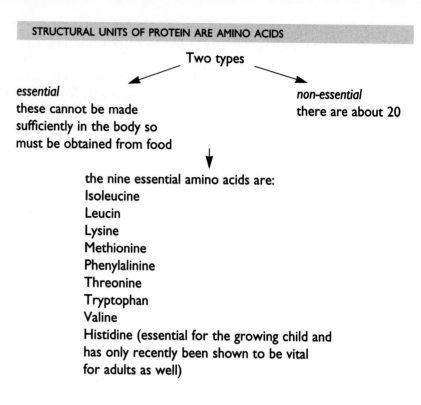

STRUCTURAL UNITS OF PROTEIN ARE AMINO ACIDS

Two types

essential
these cannot be made
sufficiently in the body so
must be obtained from food

non-essential
there are about 20

the nine essential amino acids are:
Isoleucine
Leucin
Lysine
Methionine
Phenylalinine
Threonine
Tryptophan
Valine
Histidine (essential for the growing child and
has only recently been shown to be vital
for adults as well)

Fats

Fats contain vitamins and are essential to body functioning.
Saturated fats are the least important and should be restricted.

THREE TYPES OF FATS

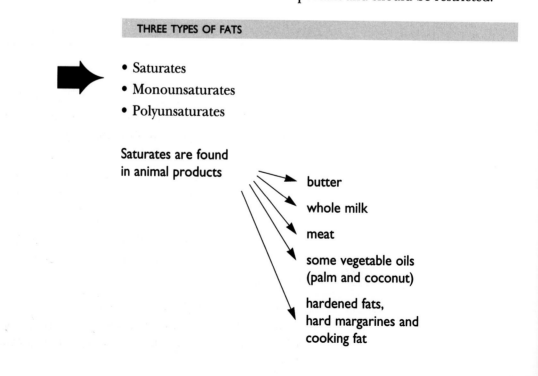

- Saturates
- Monounsaturates
- Polyunsaturates

Saturates are found
in animal products

butter

whole milk

meat

some vegetable oils
(palm and coconut)

hardened fats,
hard margarines and
cooking fat

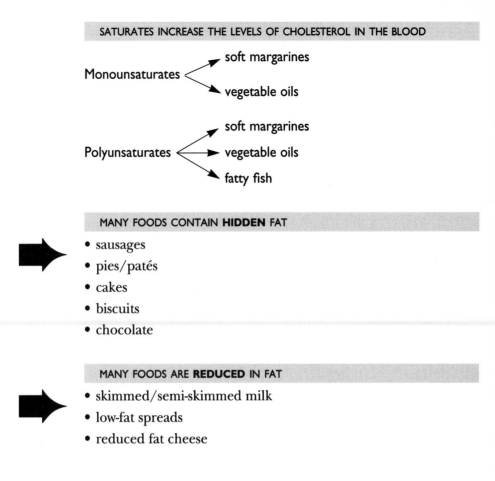

SATURATES INCREASE THE LEVELS OF CHOLESTEROL IN THE BLOOD

Monounsaturates
- soft margarines
- vegetable oils

Polyunsaturates
- soft margarines
- vegetable oils
- fatty fish

MANY FOODS CONTAIN **HIDDEN** FAT

- sausages
- pies/patés
- cakes
- biscuits
- chocolate

MANY FOODS ARE **REDUCED** IN FAT

- skimmed/semi-skimmed milk
- low-fat spreads
- reduced fat cheese

WHAT IS FAT?

Fat is made up of different types of **fatty acids** with different chemical compositions, consisting of a chain of carbon atoms to which hydrogen atoms are attached, along with some other components.

Saturated fatty acids or **saturates** are chains of carbon atoms to which a maximum number of hydrogen atoms are attached.

Unsaturated fatty acids or **unsaturates** are a chain of carbon atoms with two or more hydrogen atoms missing. This group includes:

- monounsaturates
- polyunsaturates.

Essential fatty acids (linoleic and a-linolenic acids) are polyunsaturated fatty acids which are required by the body but which cannot be made in the body. They must therefore be supplied by food.

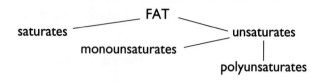

Estimated Average Requirements (EARs) for energy, fat, saturated fat and sugar (non-milk extrinsic sugars) per day

	Males					Females				
	kcals	fat (g)	saturated fat (g)	sugar (NME) (g)	fibre (NSP) (g)	kcals	fat (g)	saturated fat (g)	sugar (NME) (g)	fibre (NSP) (g)
1–3 years	1,230	45	14	33	(i)	1,165	43	13	31	(i)
4–6 years	1,715	63	19	46	(i)	1,545	57	17	41	(i)
7–10 years	1,970	72	22	53	(i)	1,740	64	19	46	(i)
11–14 years	2,220	81	25	59	18	1,845	68	21	49	18
15–18 years	2,755	101	31	73	18	2,110	77	23	56	18
19–50 years	2,550	94	28	68	18	1,940	71	22	52	18
51–59 years	2,550	94	28	68	18	1,900	70	21	51	18
60–64 years	2,380	87	26	63	18	1,900	70	21	51	18
65–74 years	2,330	85	26	62	18	1,900	70	21	51	18
75+ years	2,100	77	23	56	18	1,810	66	20	48	18

Fat based on 33 per cent of total energy intake.
Saturated fat based on 10 per cent of total energy intake.
Non-milk extrinsic sugar based on 10 per cent of total energy intake.

(i) It is recommended that children should have proportionately less non-starch polysaccharides and that children of less than two years should not take foods rich in NSP at the expense of more energy-rich foods, required for adequate growth.

Source: Dietary Reference Values for Food Energy and Nutrients for the United Kingdom, HMSO, London (1991). Reproduced with the permission of the Controller, HMSO.

Calorie, fat and saturated fat contents of meat, poultry and fish, per serving

Food	Calories	Total fat (grams)	Saturated fat (grams)
Meat and meat products			
Bacon			
1 rasher, grilled, lean only, 25g	73	4.7	1.9
1 rasher, back, grilled, lean and fat, 25g	101	8.5	3.3
Beef			
topside, roast, lean only, 100g	156	4.4	1.4
topside, roast, lean and fat, 100g	214	12.0	4.1

Poultry	Calories	Total fat (grams)	Saturated fat (grams)
chicken, roast, no skin, 100g	148	5.4	1.6
chicken, roast, meat and skin, 100g	216	14.0	4.2
duck, roast, meat and skin, 100g	339	29.0	7.9
Lamb			
leg, roast, lean only, 100g	191	8.1	3.9
shoulder, roast, lean and fat, 100g	316	26.3	13.1
Pork			
chop, grilled, lean only, 100g	226	10.7	3.8
leg, roast, lean and fat, 100g	286	19.8	7.3
leg, roast, lean only, 100g	185	6.9	2.4
Offal			
liver, lamb's, fried, 100g	232	14.0	4.0
Other meat products			
corned beef, 100g	217	12.1	6.3
ham, tinned, 100g	120	5.1	1.9
liver sausage, 100g	310	26.9	7.9
pork pie, individual, 140g	526	37.8	14.3
sausages, pork, grilled, 1 large, 60g	191	14.8	5.7
sausage roll, 1 medium, 60g	286	21.8	8.0
steak & kidney pie, individual, 200g	646	42.4	16.8

Fish and fish products

White fish	Calories	Total fat (grams)	Saturated fat (grams)
cod, poached, medium portion, 120g	113	1.3	0.5
cod, fried in batter in veg. oil, 180g	358	18.5	1.6
cod, fried in batter in lard, 180g	358	18.5	8.5
Oily fish			
herring, grilled, 1 medium, 120g	240	15.6	4.4
mackerel, smoked, 1 medium, 150g	531	46.3	9.4
pilchards, tinned in tomato sauce, 100g	126	5.4	1.1
salmon, tinned, 100g	155	8.2	1.5
sardines, tinned in oil, drained, 100g	217	13.6	2.8
trout, brown, steamed, 1 average, 180g	160	5.4	1.3
tuna, tinned in brine, 100g	99	0.6	0.2
tuna, tinned in oil, drained, 100g	189	9.0	1.4
Shellfish (weight without shell)			
prawns, boiled, 56g	60	1.0	0.2
scampi, fried in veg. oil, 150g	474	26.4	2.5
Fish products			
fish fingers, 2 grilled, 56g	120	5.0	1.6
taramasalata, 1 tbs, 45g	200	20.9	1.4

Source: The Composition of Foods, 5th ed. (1991). Reproduced with the permission of the Royal Society of Chemistry and the Controller of HMSO.

Calorie, fat and saturated fat contents of dairy products and eggs, per serving

Food	Calories	Total fat (grams)	Saturated fat (grams)
Milk per half pint/285ml			
full fat	188	11.1	6.8
semi-skimmed	131	4.6	2.8
skimmed	94	0.3	0.3
Cream per 142ml/5oz carton			
double	638	68.2	42.6
whipping	530	55.8	34.9
single	281	27.1	16.9
Cheese per 50g serving			
cream	220	23.7	14.9
Stilton	206	17.8	11.1
Cheddar type	206	17.2	10.9
Danish Blue type	174	14.8	9.2
Brie	160	13.5	8.4
Edam	166	12.7	8.0
reduced fat hard, e.g. Tendale	130	7.5	4.7
cottage	49	2.0	1.2
fromage frais, very low fat	29	0.1	0.1
Egg per size 2 egg			
boiled	88	6.5	1.9
fried in veg. oil	107	8.3	2.4
Yoghurt per 150g carton			
Greek	172	13.6	7.8
fruit	135	1.0	0.6
low fat natural	84	1.2	0.7

Source: The Composition of Foods, 5th ed. (1991). Reproduced with the permission of the Royal Society of Chemistry and the Controller of HMSO.

Carbohydrates

The main function of carbohydrates is to provide the body's energy. The brain and nervous system cannot use other nutrients for energy purposes.

What are carbohydrates?

Three types are:

1 monosaccharides (sugars)
2 disaccharides (sugars)
3 polysaccharides (complex carbohydrate)

MONOSACCHARIDES ARE SIMPLE OR SINGLE SUGARS.

glucose, fructose and galactose
↓
glucose is found in fruit and some root vegetables
↓
most carbohydrates are broken down to
glucose when digested
↓
glucose is the best form of sugar for immediate energy
↓
fructose is found with glucose
in honey and fruit
↓
galactose is a component of lactose (milk sugar)

DISACCHARIDES ARE MADE UP OF TWO MONOSACCHARIDES JOINED
TOGETHER.

most important disaccharides are
sucrose, lactose and maltose
↓
sucrose is found in table sugar
and in some vegetables and fruit
↓
lactose occurs only in milk
and milk products
↓
maltose is made when
starch is broken down by digestion

Complex carbohydrates consist of:

- **polysaccharides** (starches digestible)
- **polysaccharides** (non starch = NSP, fibre)

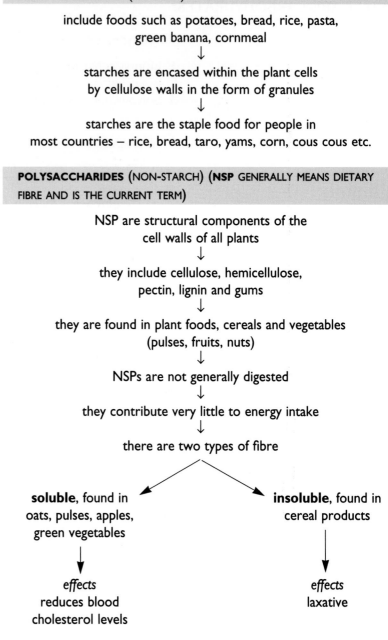

POLYSACCHARIDES (STARCHES)

include foods such as potatoes, bread, rice, pasta,
green banana, cornmeal
↓
starches are encased within the plant cells
by cellulose walls in the form of granules
↓
starches are the staple food for people in
most countries – rice, bread, taro, yams, corn, cous cous etc.

POLYSACCHARIDES (NON-STARCH) (**NSP** GENERALLY MEANS DIETARY FIBRE AND IS THE CURRENT TERM)

NSP are structural components of the
cell walls of all plants
↓
they include cellulose, hemicellulose,
pectin, lignin and gums
↓
they are found in plant foods, cereals and vegetables
(pulses, fruits, nuts)
↓
NSPs are not generally digested
↓
they contribute very little to energy intake
↓
there are two types of fibre

soluble, found in
oats, pulses, apples,
green vegetables

insoluble, found in
cereal products

effects
reduces blood
cholesterol levels

effects
laxative

HEALTHY EATING AND CARBOHYDRATES

REDUCE

- sugar
- biscuits, cakes, sweets, chocolate

EAT MORE

- fresh fruit
- unsweetened breakfast cereal

INCREASE STARCHES

- root vegetables and pulses
- bread, potatoes

INCREASE NON-STARCH POLYSACCHARIDES (FIBRE)

- wholegrain varieties of bread, rice and pasta

Non-starch polysaccharide content of different foods, per 100g of food as eaten

Food	Total NSP per 100g of food
Breakfast cereals	
Allbran	24.5
Branflakes	13.0
Shredded Wheat	9.8
Weetabix	9.7
muesli	6.4
puffed wheat	5.6
Special K	2.0
Cornflakes	0.9
Rice Krispies	0.7
Bread	
wholemeal	5.8
granary	4.3
brown	3.5
white	1.5
Biscuits	
crispbread, rye	11.7
crackers, wholemeal	4.4
digestive	2.2
cream crackers	2.2
gingernuts	1.4
Other cereals	
spaghetti, wholemeal, boiled	3.5
spaghetti, white, boiled	1.2
rice, brown, boiled	0.8
rice, white, boiled	0.1

Vegetables

beans, red kidney, boiled	6.7
beans, broad, boiled	6.5
peas, frozen, boiled	5.1
chick peas, boiled	4.3
lentils, green, boiled	3.8
beans, baked	3.7
brussels sprouts, boiled	3.1
potatoes, jacket, with skin	2.7
carrots, boiled	2.5
lentils, red, boiled	1.9
cabbage, boiled	1.8
potatoes, boiled	1.2

Fruit and nuts

apricots, dried, ready-to-eat	6.3
peanuts, roasted	6.0
raspberries	2.5
apples	1.8
oranges	1.7
bananas	1.1

Source: The Composition of Foods, 5th ed. (1991). Reproduced with the permission of the Royal Society of Chemistry and the Controller of HMSO.

Sensible guide to alcohol consumption

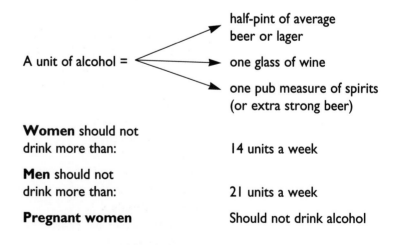

A unit of alcohol =
- half-pint of average beer or lager
- one glass of wine
- one pub measure of spirits (or extra strong beer)

Women should not drink more than: 14 units a week

Men should not drink more than: 21 units a week

Pregnant women   Should not drink alcohol

Units of energy

A **calorie** or **kilocalorie** is a unit of energy (heat).

One calorie is the amount of heat required to raise the temperature of 1 kg of water by 1°C.

INTERNATIONAL MEASUREMENT

Units of energy: the preferred term is **kilojoule** = (kJ)

Kilocalories can be converted to kilojoules by multiplying kilocalories by 4.184 (or 4.2 approximately)

2500 kilocalories × 4.184 = 10,460 kJ
2500 kilocalories is approximately 10,000 kilojoules
1000 kilojoules = 1 megajoule

THE ENERGY VALUE OF FOOD

1 gram (1g) of carbohydrate = 3.75 kilocalories
1 gram (1g) of fat = 9 kilocalories
1 gram (1g) of protein = 4 kilocalories
1 gram (1g) of alcohol = 7 kilocalories

Calorie contents of some commonly eaten foods, per average serving

	Calories
Bread and cereal products	
bread, white, 1 slice, 40g	94
wholemeal, 1 slice, 40g	86
roll, 1 crusty, 50g	140
biscuit, arrowroot, 7g	32
cream cracker, 7g	30
digestive, 17g	80
shortbread, 15g	70
cake, fruitcake, 90g	320
Danish pastry, 110g	410
doughnut, 75g	300
pizza, 200g	470
rice, boiled, 150g	210
spaghetti, boiled, 230g	240

Fats and oil

butter, average spread, 10g	74
margarine, average spread, 10g	74
low fat spread (40% fat), 10g	37
oil, vegetable, 2tsp, 10ml	90

Dairy products — See page 226

Meat and meat products — See pages 224–5

Fish — See page 225

Vegetables

baked beans, 135g	113
broccoli, 90g	22
brussels sprouts, 90g	32
cabbage, 90g	14
carrots, 90g	22
mushrooms, fried, 45g	71
peas, frozen, boiled, 90g	62
potatoes, boiled, 200g	144
potatoes, roast, 200g	298
potatoes, chipped, 200g	478
potato crisps, 1 bag, 25g	136
tomato, raw, 90g	15
tomato, fried, 90g	82

Fruit (weight without skin or stone)

apple, 1 medium, 112g	53
avocado pear, $\frac{1}{2}$ medium, 75g	142
banana, 1 medium, 100g	95
orange, 1 medium, 160g	60
peach, 1 medium, 110g	36
strawberries, 112g	30

Nuts (weight without shell)

almonds, 6 whole, 10g	61
chestnuts, 1 whole, 10g	17
peanuts, roasted, 10 whole, 10g	60

Soft drinks

lemonade, 1 can, 330ml	70
cola, 1 can, 330ml	130
orange juice, fresh, 1 glass, 200ml	72
tomato juice, 1 glass, 200ml	28

Sugar and preserves

honey, 1 average spread, 20g	58
jam, 1 average spread, 15g	39
marmalade, 1 average spread, 15g	39
sugar, 1tsp, 5g	20

Alcohol

bitter, draught, $\frac{1}{2}$ pint	90
lager, bottled, $\frac{1}{2}$ pint	82
stout, bottled, $\frac{1}{2}$ pint	105

cider, dry, $\frac{1}{2}$ pint	102
wine, dry white, 1 glass, 125ml	83
wine, medium white, 1 glass, 125ml	94
wine, red, 1 glass, 125ml	85
spirits, 1 pub measure, 24ml	53

Source: The Composition of Foods, 5th ed. (1991). Reproduced with the permission of the Royal Society of Chemistry and the Controller of HMSO.

BASIC USEFUL TERMS

Basal metabolic rate (BMR)
the rate at which the body uses energy when at complete rest

Metabolism
the chemical processes which convert the food we eat into energy

Metabolic rate
the speed at which the energy is released into the body

Catabolism
the process by which food is broken down to release energy and waste

Anabolism
the process by which the body builds, or makes new products

Digestion
the process by which food is broken down so it is small enough to be absorbed by the cells. The stages of digestion are:

- **ingestion:** food is taken through the mouth
- **digestion** begins in the mouth but takes place in the stomach and small intestine
- **absorption** is when soluble nutrients from food diffuse through the alimentary canal wall into the blood
- **excretion** is the elimination of undigested food.

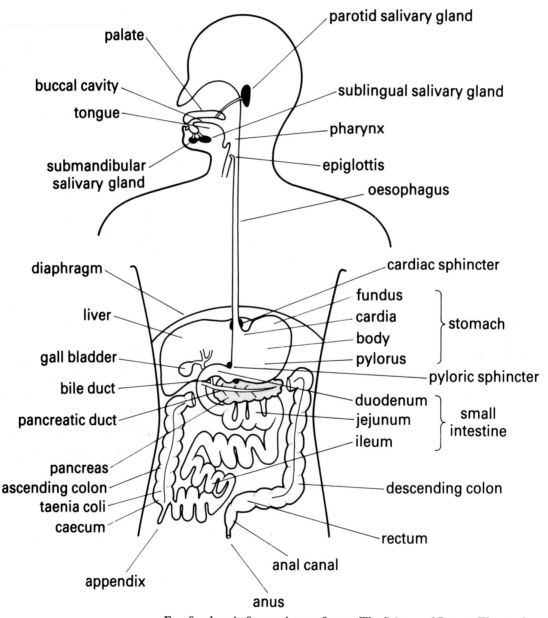

parotid salivary gland

palate

buccal cavity

tongue

sublingual salivary gland

pharynx

epiglottis

submandibular
salivary gland

oesophagus

diaphragm

cardiac sphincter

fundus

liver

cardia

body

stomach

pylorus

gall bladder

bile duct

pyloric sphincter

pancreatic duct

duodenum

jejunum

small
intestine

ileum

pancreas

ascending colon

taenia coli

descending colon

caecum

rectum

appendix

anal canal

anus

Figure 19: *The digestive system*

For further information refer to *The Science of Beauty Therapy* by
Ruth Bennett (1995), London: Hodder and Stoughton.

DIET PLAN FOR MEN

2250 CALORIE DIET PLAN

(For the moderately sedentary man, not overweight)

Allowances
Daily:

- 1 pint skimmed milk per day
- 4 medium slices wholemeal bread per day
- 2oz unsweetened wholemeal breakfast cereal per day (e.g. muesli, porridge, bran flakes)
- 8oz (2 small glasses) unsweetened fruit juice per day
- 4 portions fresh fruit per day
- 5oz (1 pot) low-fat unsweetened yoghurt per day (can be substituted for 1 extra slice of bread if preferred)
- 1lb (2 large) potatoes per day cooked in skins (3oz rice or pasta can be substituted for potato)
- 4oz (4 level tbsp cooked) pulses per day (e.g. baked beans, kidney beans, lentils, peas, butter beans)
- Fresh green salad and vegetables as desired

Weekly:

- 6oz butter per week
- 1 oz (2tbsp) sunflower oil per week
- 4oz (4 level tbsp) dried fruit per week
- 4oz (2 very small packets) nuts per week (choose from almonds, peanuts, walnuts, hazelnuts)

'Light' meal:
choose one of the following:
    4oz (small pot) cottage cheese
or 3oz white fish, lean ham or poultry
or 2 oz lean bacon, beef, pork or lamb

'Main' meal
choose one of the following:
    6 oz cottage cheese
or 6oz white fish
or 4oz lean beef, lamb, pork or poultry
or 4oz oily fish (e.g. mackerel, herring)
or 3oz Camembert or 'hard' cheese e.g. Cheddar, Edam, Cheshire (only once per week)

- A glass of dry wine may be substituted for 1 slice of bread from allowance (max: 3 glasses per week)

Suggested Menus

Breakfast: Orange juice
Breakfast cereal
Milk from allowance
Toast with butter from allowance

Lunch: Chicken
('Light' Salad with yoghurt dressing
meal) Bread with butter from allowance
Fresh fruit

Dinner: Tomato juice or ½ grapefruit
('Main' Poached haddock
meal) Baked potato
Butter beans with mushrooms
Peas
Stewed apple with yoghurt

Between meal snacks: Fruit, bread and butter from allowance.

Breakfast: Muesli
Fresh fruit
Milk from allowance
Toast with butter from allowance

Lunch: Sandwich made with bread
('Light' and butter from allowance
meal) and filled with ham
tomato
salad
Yoghurt

Dinner: Melon
('Main' Grilled trout
meal) New potatoes
Peas, sweetcorn
Fresh fruit salad

Between meal snacks: Fruit and nuts from allowance
Bread and butter from allowance.

Drinks allowed
Soda water
Mineral water
Clear soup
Tea/coffee with milk from allowance

1500 CALORIE DIET PLAN

(For the overweight, moderately sedentary man)

Allowances
Daily:

- 1 pint skimmed milk per day ½ pint milk can be substituted for 5oz low-fat unsweetened yoghurt)
- 4 medium slices wholemeal bread per day
- 1½oz unsweetened wholemeal breakfast cereal (e.g. muesli, porridge, bran flakes)
- 8oz (2 small glasses) unsweetened fruit juice per day
- 3 portions fresh fruit per day
- 8oz (1 large) potato per day cooked in skin
- Fresh green salad and vegetables as desired

Weekly:

- 3½oz butter per week
- 3oz (3 level tbsp) dried fruit per week
- 3oz (1½ small bags) nuts per week (choose from almonds, peanuts, hazelnuts, walnuts)
- 3oz (3 level tbsp cooked) pulses, three times per week (e.g. baked beans, kidney beans, lentils, peas, butter beans)

'Light' meal
choose one of the following:
    4oz cottage cheese
or 3oz white fish, lean ham or poultry
or 2oz lean bacon, beef, pork or lamb

'Main' meal
choose one of the following:
    4oz cottage cheese
or 4oz white fish
or 3oz lean pork, lamb or poultry
or 4oz oily fish (e.g. mackerel or herring)
or 1oz Camembert or 'hard' cheese such as Cheddar, Edam, Cheshire (only once per week)

- No alcohol

DIET PLAN FOR WOMEN

2000 CALORIE DIET PLAN

(For the moderately sedentary woman, not overweight)

Allowances

Daily:

- 1 pint skimmed milk per day
- 4 medium slices wholemeal bread per day
- 2oz unsweetened wholemeal breakfast cereal (e.g. muesli, porridge, bran flakes)
- 8oz (2 small glasses) unsweetened fruit juice per day
- 4 portions fresh fruit per day
- 5oz (1 pot) low-fat unsweetened yoghurt per day (this can be substituted for an extra slice of bread)
- 10oz (3 small) potatoes per day cooked in skins (1oz rice or 1oz pasta can be substituted for 1 potato)
- 4oz (4 level tbsp cooked) pulses per day (e.g. baked beans, kidney beans, lentils, peas, butter beans)
- Fresh green salad and vegetables as desired

Weekly:

- 4oz butter per week
- 1oz (2tbsp) sunflower oil per week
- 4oz (4 level tbsp) dried fruit per week
- 4oz (2 very small bags) nuts per week (choose from almonds, peanuts, hazelnuts, walnuts)

'Light' meal

choose one of the following:
    4oz cottage cheese
or 3oz white fish
or 3oz lean ham or poultry
or 2oz lean beef, pork or lamb

'Main' meal:

choose one of the following:
    6oz cottage cheese
or 6oz white fish
or 4oz lean beef, lamb, pork or poultry
or 4oz oily fish (e.g. mackerel, herring)
or 3oz Camembert or 'hard' cheeses such as Cheddar, Edam, Cheshire (once per week only)

- Alcohol: A glass of dry wine may be substituted for a slice of bread from allowance: max 2 glasses per week

Suggested Menus

Breakfast:	Orange juice Breakfast cereal with milk from allowance Toast/bread with butter from allowance
Lunch: ('Light' meal)	Lean ham Salad with yoghurt dressing Bread with butter from allowance Fresh fruit
Dinner: ('Main' meal)	Tomato juice or ½ grapefruit Roast chicken (remove skin) Baked potato Kidney beans Peas Stewed apple with yoghurt
Between meal snacks:	Fruit, bread and butter from allowance.
Breakfast:	Orange juice Toast and butter from allowance Grilled bacon and tomato
Lunch: ('Light' meal)	Tuna in brine Mixed salad with dressing using oil from allowance Bread and butter from allowance Fruit
Dinner: ('Main' meal)	Lentil and vegetable curry Brown rice or potatoes Salad Fruit
Before bed:	Cereal and milk from allowance
Between meal snacks:	Fruit, bread and butter from allowance.

Drinks allowed

Soda water
Mineral water
Tea/coffee with milk from allowance

1000 CALORIE DIET PLAN

(For the overweight, moderately sedentary woman)

Allowances

Daily:

- ¾pt skimmed milk per day
- 2 medium slices wholemeal bread per day
- 1oz unsweetened wholemeal breakfast cereal per day (e.g. muesli, porridge, bran flakes)
- 4oz (1 small glass) unsweetened fruit juice per day
- 3 portions fresh fruit per day
- 5oz (2 small) potatoes per day, cooked in skins
- Fresh green salad and vegetables as desired

Weekly:

- 1¾oz butter per week
- 1oz (1 level tbsp) dried fruit per week

'Light' meal:

choose from one of the following:
    4 days per week as for main meal, above
    3 days per week: 3 oz (3 level tbsp cooked) baked beans, lentils, butter beans or other pulses

'Main' meal:

choose from one of the following:
    4oz cottage cheese
or 3oz white fish
or 3oz lean ham, chicken or turkey
or 2oz lean beef, pork or lamb

- No alcohol

RECORD CHART
DAILY FOOD AND DRINK

	BREAKFAST	SNACKS	LUNCH	SNACKS	DINNER	OTHER
MONDAY						
TUESDAY						
WEDNESDAY						
THURSDAY						
FRIDAY						
SATURDAY						
SUNDAY						

Figure 20:   *Example of a daily food chart*

CHAPTER 29 *The science of electromagnetic treatment*

The electromagnetic spectrum

The sun's energy – radiation – travels as a variety of wavelengths through space. This is called the **electromagnetic spectrum**:

- cosmic rays
- gamma rays
- x-rays
- ultra-violet
- visible light
- infra-red
- radar
- long radio waves

ELECTROMAGNETIC WAVES

Electromagnetic waves transmit:

- heat
- light
- sound.

The waves vary in length and can be measured by:

- an **angstrom unit** (Å) – one ten-millionth of a millimetre

or

- a **nanometre** (nm) – one millionth of a millimetre

An angstrom equals a tenth of a nanometre.

Other terms are:

The **wavelength** – the distance travelled by the wave in one complete cycle – that is the point on one wave to the same point on the next wave.

As the wavelength increases the frequency decreases and as the wavelength decreases the frequency increases.

The **frequency** – the number of cycles that take place in a unit of time. This is measured in **cycles per second** or **hertz**.

Electromagnetic energy travels as straight-line rays.

Within this straight line the energy cycles in regular waves pulsating at right angles to the direction of travel.

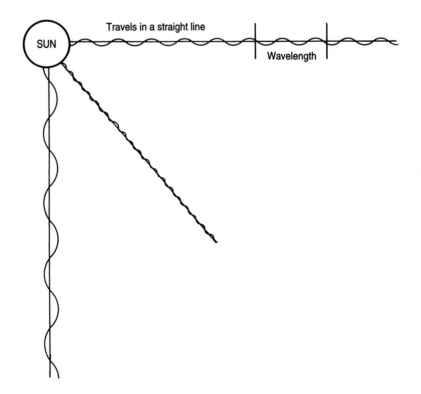

Figure 21:   *Electromagnetic energy*

THE ELECTROMAGNETIC SPECTRUM

Ultraviolet rays
200–280 nm UVC

Invisible to the naked eye,
colder and **shorter** when visible
light is added – blue rays can be seen

Visible light rays
400–700 nm

violet
indigo
blue
green
yellow
orange
red

Lies in the
middle of
the spectrum

(rays are **longer**
than UV rays)

Infra-red rays
700 nm–4000 nm

Have a **longer** wavelength than
visible light. They are:

not visible
felt as heat

(radiant heat is produced by
adding visible light)

ULTRA-VIOLET RAYS AND THE SKIN

The rays	What they do	Effects
UVA rays (long) are invisible to the naked eye	They produce a tan by stimulating the melanin in the skin	They penetrate the dermis and collagen and elastic fibres are damaged. The skin loses its structural support
UVB rays (medium) only penetrate the epidermis	They produce a tan. They make cells produce more melanin	They cause sunburn. These rays are the cause of skin cancers
UVC rays (short) do not reach the earth	They are destructive to living/human tissue	They are used for sterilisation processes. Dangerous to skin

NATURAL SUNLIGHT AND ITS EFFECT ON THE SKIN

Moderate exposure to natural sunlight can:

- stimulate chemical activity in the skin
- stimulate the production of vitamin D (which is vital for healthy bones)
- produce a suntan and assist some skin problems.

Over-exposure to natural sunlight will:

- thicken the skin with overproduction of cells
- cause sunburn
- age the skin
- cause skin cancers in some people.

Exposure to natural sunlight should be limited and sunscreens are recommended for regular use.

SKIN TYPES

The wide range of skin types means that everyone is different.

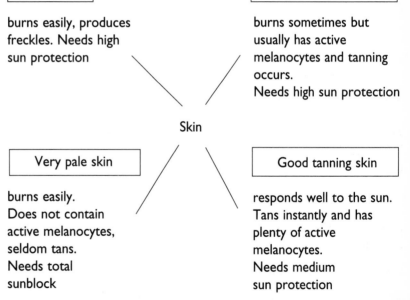

Fair skin

burns easily, produces freckles. Needs high sun protection

Sallow fair skin

burns sometimes but usually has active melanocytes and tanning occurs.
Needs high sun protection

Skin

Very pale skin

burns easily.
Does not contain active melanocytes, seldom tans.
Needs total sunblock

Good tanning skin

responds well to the sun. Tans instantly and has plenty of active melanocytes.
Needs medium sun protection

REMEMBER

- All skins need sun protection.

CHAPTER 30

Basic facts about the law in relation to operating a business

The relevant laws are:

The Factories Act 1961

The Offices, Shops and Railway Premises Act 1963

Re-sale Prices Act 1964 and 1976

Misrepresentation Act 1967

The Trade Descriptions Act 1968–72

Employers' Liability Act 1969

The Fire Precautions Act 1971

The Contracts of Employment Act 1972

Health and Safety at Work Act 1974 (HSW Act)

The Sexual Discrimination Act 1975 and 1986

The Fire Regulations Act 1976

The Race Relations Act 1976

Employment Protection (Consolidation) Act 1978

Sale of Goods Act 1979

Health and Safety (First Aid) Regulations 1981

Supply of Goods and Services Act 1982

Data Protection Act 1984

The Reporting of Injuries, Diseases and Dangerous Occurrences Regulations 1985

Consumer Protection Act 1987

COSHH – Control of Substances Hazardous to Health 1989

The Electricity at Work Regulations 1989

COSHH (Amendment) Regulations 1990, 1991, 1992

Workplace Health and Safety Welfare Regulations 1992 (EC Directives)

Minimum standards are defined in these Acts. It is the responsibility of the firm/business/employer to ensure that the law is carried out.

The Health and Safety Executive

The Health and Safety Executive appoint inspectors (or your local council will probably also have an environmental health officer) to visit workplaces **without notice** at any reasonable time, to check that an employer is adhering to the law.

INSPECTORS CAN:

- examine the safety, health and welfare aspects of a business
- investigate an accident or a complaint
- talk to employees
- take photographs and samples
- expect co-operation and answers to their questions
- impound dangerous equipment.

IF A PROBLEM IS FOUND THEY CAN:

- issue a formal notice – an **improvement notice** – and a set period of time is allowed to rectify the fault
- issue a **prohibition notice**, which means that the employee must stop the use of a process or equipment. Failure to do so could result in prosecution (the employer may appeal to an Industrial Tribunal).

REMEMBER

- inspectors have the power to **prosecute** a firm or an individual for breaking the Health and Safety laws.

DID YOU KNOW THAT

- inspectors must be notified if you are running a commercial or industrial business?
- Health and Safety Information for Employees Regulations must be displayed?
- An Employers' Liability Certificate (compulsory insurance) must be displayed?
- certain types of accidents, occupational diseases and dangerous occurrences must be reported? (see pages 248–249)
- you may need to train and appoint someone to carry out certain specific tasks
- you may need an expert – e.g. the manufacturer of a sunbed – to conduct periodic tests of equipment
- it is the **employer's** responsibility to ensure that employees follow safe working practices.

HEALTH AND SAFETY AT WORK ACT 1974

This Act requires employers, so far as is reasonably practicable, to safeguard the health, safety and welfare of all their employees.

If you are the **Employer** you must provide:

- a **safety policy** if you have five or more employees. This must show the **organisation** and the **systems and procedures** for carrying it out. The policy must be revised regularly and employees must be advised of any changes.

YOU WILL NEED TO:

- check legal requirements (refer to the Act)
- train yourself (learn to identify hazards)
- train staff (to recognise dangers)
- organise duties (see below)
- monitor this plan.

Organising duties means that you will probably have a variety of employees:

- cleaners
- receptionist
- beauty therapists
- line manager
- supervisor.

Whoever they are, make sure they know:

- **your duties** to them
- **their duties** to you.

THE EMPLOYER'S DUTY IS TO PROVIDE:

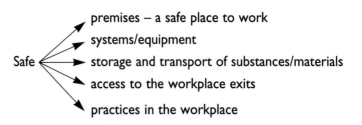

Safe
- premises – a safe place to work
- systems/equipment
- storage and transport of substances/materials
- access to the workplace exits
- practices in the workplace

The employer's duty to other persons means that persons not in employment are:

- not exposed to health and safety risks – this includes contractors, employees, self-employed persons.

THE EMPLOYEES ALSO HAVE DUTIES:

- to take care while at work to avoid personal injury
- to assist the employer in meeting the requirements of the Health and Safety Act
- not to misuse or change anything that has been provided for safety.

REMEMBER

The employee has a responsibility
↓
to her/himself
↓
to other employees
↓
to the public

In 1992 EC directives updated legislation on Health and Safety management and widened the existing Acts on Health and Safety. These came into force in 1993.

The aim was to improve Health and Safety management in all workplaces, and in particular in six existing areas with one set of regulations for each directive:

- provision and use of work equipment
- manual handling operations
- workplace health, safety and welfare
- personal protective equipment at work (PPE)
- health and safety (display screen equipment)
- management of health and safety at work.

In addition the Workplace Health and Safety Welfare Regulations 1992 included three new provisions:

- the protection of non-smokers from tobacco smoke
- the provision of rest facilities for pregnant and nursing mothers
- safe cleaning of windows.

THE KEY FOR SAFETY IN YOUR BUSINESS

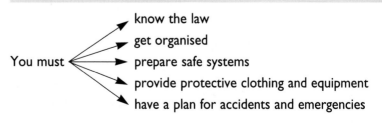

You must
- know the law
- get organised
- prepare safe systems
- provide protective clothing and equipment
- have a plan for accidents and emergencies

the general working environment

health problems

safe use of chemicals

the quality of the air

noise and vibration

radiation

You must consider ——— electricity

machine safety

fire/explosion

dangerous substances

transport and handling materials

preventing falls

regular maintenance work

ACCIDENTS IN THE WORKPLACE

THE REPORTING OF INJURIES, DISEASES AND DANGEROUS OCCURRENCES REGULATIONS 1985

The law demands that accidents in the workplace are **recorded**.
The procedure is:

date

time

place of the accident

→ full name and occupation of the person
→ details of the injury
→ a brief description of the accident

These must be recorded in an **accident record book**.

The Reporting of Injuries, Diseases and Dangerous Occurrences
Regulations 1985 state that employers and self-employed persons
must notify the enforcing authority immediately by telephone if a
serious accident occurs:

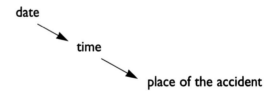

- someone dies
- receives a major injury
- poisoning
- electric shock.

A written report form (F2508) **must be** completed within seven days and sent to the Health and Safety Inspector.

REMEMBER

- always have copies of the Report Form F2508 available and ready for use.

Checkpoints:

- deal with any immediate injury/emergency
- make premises safe
- report the accident (if necessary).

BE PREPARED

In all businesses/establishments:

- there should be an accident plan
- staff should know what to do.

They need to know **who**:

- will raise the alarm
- will control the incident
- will make the premises safe
- are the key people i.e. First Aid officers.

FIRST AID

'All businesses must have an appropriate level of first aid treatment available.' Health and Safety (First Aid) Regulations, 1981.

This means for most small businesses that they **must**:

- **appoint** a person to take charge in an emergency and to look after First Aid equipment and there must be one 'appointed person' available when people are working
- **provide** and maintain a First Aid box (see below). The box should contain information/guidance on the treatment of injured people:
  - how to control bleeding
  - how to give artificial respiration
  - how to deal with unconsciousness.
- **display** notices which state:
  - locations of first aid equipment
  - name of person(s) responsible for First Aid.

Some larger businesses require a first aid room and qualified first aiders. Where businesses train first aiders they must be registered through *EMAS – the Employment Medical Advisory Service.* Check with your local Employment Medical Adviser for details.

REMEMBER

• it is the business of **everyone** to know about First Aid.

YOUR FIRST AID BOX

The contents of the box will vary according to the number of staff employed.

There are **basic items** you will require:

• one guidance/information card
• individually wrapped sterile adhesive plasters
• sterile eye pads
• large sterile dressings
• very large sterile dressings
• a triangular bandage
• bandages
• safety pins
• scissors
• tweezers.

Any other **general first aid additions** are an asset, such as:

• disposable surgical gloves
• eye bath
• sterile cotton wool
• surgical adhesive tape
• recommended antiseptic solutions
• medical wipes
• instant ice sports pack.

USEFUL INFORMATION

Emergency numbers should also be placed in the first aid box, e.g. local health centre, doctor, local hospital, in addition to local emergency services – ambulance, fire, police and so on.

The first aid box should be kept in a **damp-free**, **dust-free area**. The box must be clearly marked 'First Aid', and accessible to **all** members of staff.

THE OFFICES, SHOPS AND RAILWAY PREMISES ACT 1963

This Act, in conjunction with the Health & Safety at Work Act, relates to every part of a shop/business premises.

The Act **stipulates** the **minimum standards** to ensure a safe, healthy working environment.

All premises must be:

clean
|
well-lit
|
well-ventilated
(particularly in high humidity, for control of fumes and dust)
|
maintained at a reasonable temperature
(usually above 16°C (60°F))
|
well maintained

- Floors, passageways and stairs must be properly constructed, safe and accessible at all times.
- There must be an accessible, **unlocked** fire exit and firefighting equipment (see page 252).

THE EMPLOYER MUST PROVIDE:

- adequate washing facilities with running hot and cold water, soap and towels
- clean staff toilets (one toilet for up to five employees)
- drinking water and cups
- an area for food to be eaten
- an area for the employees' clothing to be hung
- an accessible First Aid box (see page 248)
- an accident record book (see page 246)
- controlled noise levels
- an easily read thermometer in the workplace.

ACCIDENT PREVENTION

This is an important issue. The Health and Safety at Work Act is about protecting people.

Accidents occur for two reasons:

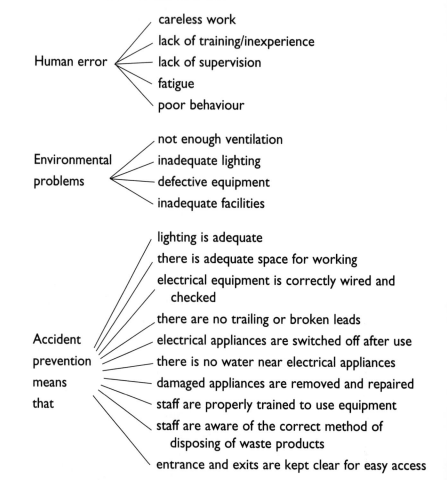

Human error
- careless work
- lack of training/inexperience
- lack of supervision
- fatigue
- poor behaviour

Environmental problems
- not enough ventilation
- inadequate lighting
- defective equipment
- inadequate facilities

Accident prevention means that
- lighting is adequate
- there is adequate space for working
- electrical equipment is correctly wired and checked
- there are no trailing or broken leads
- electrical appliances are switched off after use
- there is no water near electrical appliances
- damaged appliances are removed and repaired
- staff are properly trained to use equipment
- staff are aware of the correct method of disposing of waste products
- entrance and exits are kept clear for easy access

THE ELECTRICITY AT WORK REGULATIONS (1989)

These regulations require a business to:

- test electrical appliances once a year (minimum)
- keep the written test sheets (these could be inspected by the Health and Safety Inspector).

EMPLOYER'S LIABILITY ACT 1969 (COMPULSORY INSURANCE)

Accidents can happen at any time. Because of this fact the law requires employers to have compulsory insurance. This means that the employer is protected against claims brought by an employee who may be injured on the premises – but not if the accident is through the employees' own negligence.

A certificate of insurance **must** be displayed in the business premises.

PUBLIC LIABILITY INSURANCE

This is not statutory or compulsory, but it is advisable. This protects the employer if a member of the public is injured on the premises.

PROFESSIONAL INDEMNITY INSURANCE

Every professional beauty therapist should have this insurance protection. This is obtainable through the various professional bodies/associations in beauty and therapy. A salon owner/employer will usually include this liability in the public liability insurance policy in order to offer employees protection against claims made by clients relating to damage or personal injury resulting directly from a treatment. It is not compulsory (see pages 263–4 for details of professional bodies).

DATA PROTECTION ACT 1984

Businesses that use computers to hold personal details about their staff and clients may be required to register with the Data Protection Registrar.

The Data Protection Registrar will:

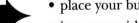

- place your business on a **public register** of data users
- issue you with a **Code of Practice** which you must comply with.

The Code of Practice stipulates that:

- you must keep the information secure
- you must ensure the information is accurate and relevant to your needs
- you must comply with individuals' requests for any information that you are holding on them.

Failure to do so means that you are contravening the Act.

Further details and registration forms are available from:

Data Protection Registrar, Springfield House, Water Lane,
Wilmslow, Cheshire SK9 5AX.
Tel: 01625 53511

FIRE REGULATIONS

The Fire Precautions Act 1971 and the Fire Regulations Act 1976
are concerned with fire prevention and the provision of suitable
exits (fire escapes).

An employer must have a fire certificate if:

- more than 20 people are employed and working
- more than ten people are working other than the ground floor.

THE EMPLOYER'S DUTY IS:

to provide a means of escape in case of fire for
staff and the public
↓
to ensure that the escape area is kept clear of
obstruction at all times
↓
to ensure the escape area is properly maintained
and all firefighting equipment is easily available
and properly maintained
↓
to ensure that all employees must be aware of the
escape route and the fire procedure in the event
of fire

REMEMBER

- check your fire alarm regularly
- have a fire drill periodically
- check fire extinguishers are operative

Information can be obtained from your local (regional) fire
department. Professional advice will be given in relation to your
business.

FIRE PREVENTION IN THE BUSINESS PREMISES

- **No smoking notices** should be displayed throughout the business (industry demands that smoking is discouraged in the workplace).
- **Be careful** with wet articles, e.g. towels and headbands. These should **never be placed** over heaters to dry.
- **Check** electrical appliances are turned off when they are not required e.g. wax heater.
- **Never** overload electrical circuits.
- **Know** where fire extinguishers are kept; which one to use; how to use it.

In salons there are usually three types of fire extinguishers.

1. Carbon dioxide (CO_2 gas). This can be used for burning liquid or electrical fires.
2. Dry powder. This can be used for electrical fires or burning liquid.
3. Foam or water. This can only be used for wood, paper or textiles, but should not be used near electrical appliances.

Other firefighting equipment includes **a glassfibre blanket** which can quickly extinguish a small fire.

- PRACTISE evacuation procedure – as follows:

If a fire starts   **stop**
                    think

Q *Is it very small?*

A If yes, fetch the appropriate firefighting equipment and take action.

Q *Is it big? Too large to attempt fighting it yourself?*

A If yes, then stay calm

- raise the alarm
- get your client(s) to safety (outside)
- leave the salon quickly
- turn off electrical appliances if possible
- close windows if there is time
- close doors as you leave.

NEXT

- dial 999, emergency services
- **ask** for the fire service
- **give** clear instructions i.e. the address of the business
- **wait** – you may be asked to repeat something or to answer questions.

As a **supervisor** it is your responsibility to ensure that your staff:

- know the evacuation procedure
- can carry out the evacuation procedure
- feel confident in an emergency
- know the order of delegation in an emergency, that is, who does what, who follows whom.

CONTROL OF SUBSTANCES HAZARDOUS TO HEALTH ACT (COSHH) 1989

This law protects the individual from exposure to hazardous substances in the workplace.

Both the **employer** and **employee** must be aware of the potential hazard of some substances and the necessary safety precautions that must be taken.

Hazardous substances are marked with symbols for your safety – **make sure you know them**.

Figure 22:   *Symbols for hazardous substances*

Hazardous substances can:

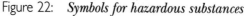

- burn skin
- cause blindness
- irritate nasal passages
- **kill** if fumes are inhaled.

Hazardous substances are:

- cleaning materials
- some beauty products (e.g. nail varnish removers)

REMEMBER

- know your 'substances' (products)
- check the health hazard caution
- handle and store all substances correctly
- dispose of them correctly and safely

This could save a life – **your life**.

RE-SALE PRICES ACT 1964–1976

These Acts state that manufacturers and wholesalers cannot make retailers sell their goods at a fixed price. They can only suggest suitable prices.

If retailers choose to sell their stock below the manufacturer's recommended price suppliers are not able to withhold stock from the retailer.

An exception to this is if it is 'in the public interest' that the suppliers can set a price.

THE TRADE DESCRIPTIONS ACT 1968–72

This Act is concerned with the false description of goods. It is a crime to mislead the public. The law says that the **retailer** must not:

- supply misleading information
- falsely describe or make false statements about products or services.

This includes ——— advertisements
                    verbal descriptions
                    display charts

and relates to ——— quality
                    quantity and
                    purpose

The retailer **must**:

- not make false comparisons between present and former prices
- not offer products at half-price unless they have already been offered at the actual price for at least twenty-eight days
- be aware of statements saying that something is 'our price' and it is worth 'double the amount'
- be aware that price comparisons are misleading and can be illegal.

The Trades Description Act 1972 stipulates that products must be labelled with the country of origin.

SALE OF GOODS ACT 1979

This Act identifies the Contract of Sale between the retailer (the business) and the consumer (client) when a product is bought.

The law says that the retailer:

- is responsible for ensuring that the goods sold are not defective
- must refund the money for the product if it is found to be defective (usually the retailer offers to replace the goods)
- must then make a complaint to the supplier.

SUPPLY OF GOODS AND SERVICES ACT 1982

This Act deals with consumers' rights and traders' obligations. It extends the protection for consumers provided by the Sale of Goods Act 1979.

The Act has two parts:

- Part 1 refers to goods
- Part 2 refers to services

PART 1 – GOODS

This means that the consumer/client is entitled to claim back some or all of her/his money from the trader/retailer if the goods do not meet certain requirements. Goods must be:

- of merchantable quality
- fit for any particular purpose made known to the supplier
- as described.

This applies to all goods supplied:

- on hire
- in part exchange
- as part of a service.

PART 2 – SERVICES

This means that the person providing the service must do so:

- for a reasonable charge
- within a reasonable time
- with reasonable care and skill.

The consumer/client must follow a particular procedure if there is a complaint.

1 Return to the supplier if not satisfied.
2 Contact a consumer adviser at a trading standards department.

CONSUMER PROTECTION ACT 1987

This Act aims to safeguard the consumer from products that do not reach a reasonable level of safety.

The salon owner must be aware of this in relation to **product liability**. Part 1 of this Act relates to product liability.

Before 1987 an injured person had to prove a manufacturer negligent before she/he could sue for damages. This Act removes the need to prove negligence.

These directives on product liability are implemented in this Act and it provides similar protection for people in the European Community. The injured person can take action against:

- producers
- importers
- own branders.

Suppliers such as:

- wholesalers
- retailers

are only liable if they do not identify the producer or own brander if asked to do so by the injured person. Goods/products used in the workplace are also included in this Act as well as the components and raw materials of a product.

In the salon this means that:

- only reputable products should be used and sold
- care should be given in handling, maintaining and storing products to ensure that they remain (whilst in use) in good condition.

It is the supervisory person's job to ensure that this is checked and monitored.

This Act is a very important one for the salon owner/retailer/supplier. It is particularly important that **staff** are familiar with the procedure as specified in the Act.

This means that:

- products
- treatments

should be sold with skill and expertise, because the client has the right to question any service or sales product if she/he feels that reasonable care and consideration has not been given.

It is the supervisory person's job to ensure that staff are always fully aware of the consumer's or client's rights.

Employment legislation

THE CONTRACT OF EMPLOYMENT

When an employee agrees to take up a working position she/he should be offered a **written contract** to confirm the terms of employment.

The Contracts of Employment Act 1972 and the Employment Protection (Consolidation) Act 1978 states the **minimum details** that must be included in the written statement/contract are:

- name of employer
- name of employee
- date employment began
- any employment with a previous employer which counts as part of the employee's continuous period of employment and, if so, the date at which the period of continuous employment began
- title of job
- hours of work
- rate of pay including overtime, commission and frequency of payment

- sick pay (terms)
- holiday pay
- holiday entitlement
- pension information or scheme
- disciplinary and grievance procedures
- safety rules
- length of notice for termination of employment.

Other contracts are:

- **open-ended contracts**

These are for an unspecified period of time and are terminable by either side, giving a period of notice as stated in the contract.

- **fixed-term contracts**

These are for set period of time and employment will automatically come to an end when the contract expires.

- **short-term contracts**

These are for three months or less. If the employee is offered repeated short-term contracts this is regarded by law as continuous employment.

THE EMPLOYMENT PROTECTION (CONSOLIDATION) ACT 1978

This Act stipulates the required period of notice that must be given by the employer and the employee.

THE EMPLOYER MUST GIVE:

- one week's notice or one week's salary in lieu of notice if the employee has worked for four weeks
- one week's notice for each year worked up to a maximum of twelve weeks if the employee has been with the business for over two years.

THE EMPLOYEE MUST GIVE:

- one week's notice after four weeks employment (unless the contract of employment states otherwise). The employee's request can be oral or written. The employer must reply to the request.

Other acts relating to employment

THE SEXUAL DISCRIMINATION ACT 1975 AND 1986

These Acts advise that it is an **offence** to discriminate between married or unmarried women and men.

THE RACE RELATIONS ACT 1976

This Act says that an employer cannot discriminate against employees on the grounds of:

- colour
- race
- nationality.

MISREPRESENTATION ACT 1967

A person entering into a contract is protected by the Misrepresentation Act.

A claim can be made if a person claims misrepresentation of terms and suffers damage.

EQUAL PAY ACT 1970

This Act states that employees who do the **same** work:

- must be employed on the same pay
- must be employed on the same terms.

FAIR AND UNFAIR DISMISSAL

FAIR DISMISSAL MEANS THAT:

- the employer must have acted reasonably
- there is sufficient reason for dismissal
- the reason was fair.

CORRECT PROCEDURE WAS FOLLOWED IF THE EMPLOYEE WAS WARNED AT LEAST THREE TIMES:

an informal verbal warning
↓
a formal verbal warning
↓
a formal written warning
↓
a final written warning

On each occasion the employee should be given the opportunity to improve.

Dismissal would be fair if after all these warnings there had still been no improvement. Then the correct notice of dismissal would be given according to the length of employment (see page 259).

Common reasons for fair dismissal

- continual poor timekeeping
- poor attendance
- unacceptable conduct
- deliberate damage to the business (equipment or property or customer relations)

Common reasons for unfair dismissal

- if the employee is pregnant and is not allowed to return to work
- being dismissed without a stated reason
- a new business owner wishes to replace an employee
- an employee has been unfairly or illegally selected for redundancy e. g. because of sex, race, religion

Immediate dismissal

This is acceptable only for gross misconduct such as **stealing**.

See Department of Employment booklet PL714.

Sources of information

Advisory Conciliation and Arbitration Service (ACAS),
Head Office,
Clifton House,
83 Euston Road,
London, NW1
Tel: 0171 388 5100

Business in the Community,
227a City Road,
London EC1V 1LX

Office of Fair Trading,
Consumer Credit Licensing Branch,
Government Building,
Bromyard Avenue,
London W3 7BB
Tel: 0181 242 2858

Foodsense,
London SE99 7TT
Tel: 01645 556000

Health and Safety Executive (HSE),
Baynards House,
1 Chepstow Place,
Westbourne Grove,
London W2
Tel: 0171 221 0870

Health Education Council,
Hamilton House,
Mabledon Place,
London WC1H 9TZ

Sports Council,
16 Upper Woburn Place,
London WC1H OQP

Trades Union Congress (TUC),
Congress House,
Great Russell Street,
London WC1B 3LS
Tel: 0171 636 4030

List of associations

Association of British Insurers,
Aldermary House,
Queen Street,
London EC4N 1TT

Association of Reflexologists,
27 Old Gloucester Street,
London WC1N 3XX

British Association of Beauty Therapy and Cosmetology,
Parabola House, Parabola Road,
Cheltenham,
Gloucestershire GL50 3AH

British Association of Electrolysists,
8 Chaul End Road,
Caddington,
Bedfordshire LU1 4AS

British Association of Skin Camouflage,
25 Blackhorse Drive,
Silkstone Common,
Barnsley,
South Yorkshire S75 4SD

British Safety Council,
National Safety Centre,
Chancellors Road,
London W6 9RS
Tel: 0171 741 1231

Federation of Image Consultants,
6 Victoria Street,
St. Albans,
Hertfordshire AL1 3JB

Independent Beauty Schools Association,
PO Box 781,
London SW3 2PN

Independent Professional Therapists International (I.P.T.I.),
8 Ordsall Road,
Retford,
Nottinghamshire DN22 7PL
Tel: 01777 700383

International Aestheticiennes,
Bache Hall,
Bache Hall Estate,
Chester,
Cheshire CH2 1BP

International Council of Health and Beauty Therapists,
38A Portsmouth Road,
Woolston,
Southampton,
Hampshire SO19 9AD

International Federation of Aromatherapists,
2 Chiswick High Road,
London W4 1TH

International Federation of Crystal and Complementary Therapists,
11 Heather Close,
New Haw,
Addlestone,
Surrey KT15 3PF

International Nail Association,
101 Moore Park Road,
Fulham,
London SW6 2DA

International Society of Professional Aromatherapists,
Hinckley & District Hospital & Health Centre,
The Annex,
Mount Road,
Hinckley,
Leicestershire LE10 1AG

National Beauty Therapy Lecturers Association,
Valerie Stables,
Hendon College,
Cornermead,
Grahame Parkway,
Collindale,
London
Tel: 0181 200 8300

Royal Society for the Prevention of Accidents (ROSPA),
Cannon House,
The Priory, Queensway,
Birmingham B4 6BS
Tel: 0121 233 2461

Recruitment

Health & Beauty Recruitment Ltd.,
28 Bolton Street,
Mayfair,
London W1Y 8HB
Tel: 0171 491 9771/2

Steiner (Careers at Sea) Group Ltd.,
57–65 The Broadway,
Stanmore,
Middlesex HA7 4DU

Magazines

Health & Beauty Salon,
Quadrant House,
The Quadrant,
Sutton,
Surrey SM2 5AS
Tel: 0181 661 3500

International Journal of Aromatherapy,
PO Box 746,
Hove,
East Sussex BN3 3XA
Tel: 01273 772479

Les Nouvelles Esthetiques,
Exhibition House,
Spring Street,
London W2 3RB
Tel: 0171 262 2886

Awarding bodies

Business and Technology Education Council,
Central House,
Upper Woburn Place,
London WC1H 0HH
Tel: 0171 413 8400

City and Guilds London Institute,
46 Britannia Street,
London WC1 9RG
Tel: 0171 278 2468

Confederation of International Beauty Therapy and Cosmetology,
Mrs D. Parkes,
Parabola House,
Parabola Road,
Cheltenham,
Gloucestershire GL50 3AH
Tel: 01242 570284

International Aestheticiennes,
Bache Hall,
Bache Hall Estate,
Chester CH2 2BR
Tel: 01244 376539

International Therapy Examination Council,
James House,
Oakelbrook Hill,
Newent,
Gloucestershire GL18 1HD
Tel: 01531 821875

National Council for Vocational Qualifications,
222 Euston Road,
London NW1 2BZ
Tel: 0171 387 9898

Scottish Vocational Education Council,
Hanover House,
24 Douglas Street,
Glasgow G2 7NQ
Tel: 0141 248 7900

Vocational Awards International,
46 Aldwick Road,
Bognor Regis,
West Sussex,
England,
PO21 2PN

Further reading

Health Education Authority, *Scientific Basis of Nutrition Education*
Health Education Authority, *Enjoy Healthy Eating*
Department of Health, HMSO, *Dietary Reference Values*
Health Education Council, *Obesity and Overweight*
Health Education Council, *Sugars in the Diet*
Health Education Council, *Starch and Dietary Fibre*

Wendy Doyle, *Nutrition: An Introduction*, Hodder & Stoughton
Iris Rigazzi-Tarling, *Creating an Excellent Salon*, Hodder & Stoughton, 1994
Ruth Bennett, *The Science of Beauty Therapy*, Hodder & Stoughton
Mo Rosser, *Body Fitness and Exercise*, Hodder & Stoughton
Bill Tancred, *Health Related Fitness*, Hodder & Stoughton
Corbin & Lindsey, *Fitness for Life*, Teachers Edition, Scott, Foresman & Co, 2nd Edition
David G. Thomas, *Swimming (Steps to Success)*, Leisure Press, 1989
Fox, Bowers & Foss, *The Physiological Basis for Exercise and Sport*, 5th Edition, Brown and Bencemari, 1992
Health Education Council, *How to protect your skin from sun damage*, (booklet)
Dr. Gordon Jackson, *Family Guide to Healthy Living, Fitness and Exercise*, Salamander, 1985
The Butter Council, *Fitness for Life* (booklet),
Department of Health, 1994 *The Health of the Nation* 'Eat Well'
Health Education Council, *Look after your Heart*
St. John's Ambulance and British Red Cross Society, *First Aid Manual*

Business related titles
Di Kamp, *Successful appraisals in a week*, Hodder & Stoughton
Mo Shapiro, *Successful interviewing in a week*, Hodder & Stoughton
Malcolm Peel, *Successful training in a week*, Hodder & Stoughton
John Wellemin, *Successful customer care in a week*, Hodder & Stoughton
Christine Harvey, *Successful selling in a week*, Hodder & Stoughton

INDEX

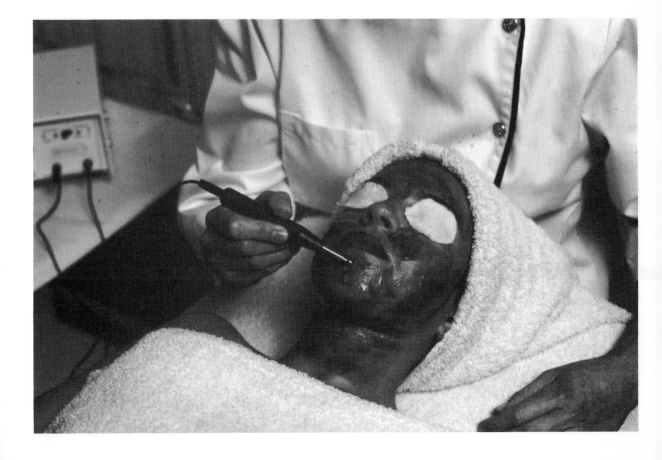